timber in contemporary architecture
a designer's guide

Peter Ross, President of TRADA

Giles Downes, Sidell Gibson Architects

Andrew Lawrence, Arup

TRADA Technology Ltd
Chiltern House
Stocking Lane
Hughenden Valley
High Wycombe
Buckinghamshire HP14 4ND

tel: +44 (0)1494 569600
fax: +44 (0)1494 565487
email: information@trada.co.uk

ISBN 978-1-900510-66-0

Published in 2009 by TRADA Technology Ltd.
Whilst every effort is made to ensure the accuracy of the advice given, the company cannot accept liability for loss or damage arising from the information supplied.

Mixed Sources
Product group from well-managed forests, controlled sources and recycled wood or fibre
www.fsc.org Cert no. SGS-COC-005091
© 1996 Forest Stewardship Council

All photographs are © Peter Ross except those otherwise credited in the captions.

All other illustrations are © TRADA Technology except those otherwise credited in the captions.

Every attempt has been made to trace the owners of copyrights, but it has proved impossible to identify Figure 4.15. Notified errors and omissions will be rectified in future editions.

Layout by Monica Bratt of Pagewise.

The authors

Peter Ross BSc, DIC, CEng, MICE
Formerly an Associate Director of Ove Arup, and now a consultant to Arup.
He is currently President of TRADA, and a member of the panel of judges for
the annual Wood Awards scheme. He is also a member of the BSI Timber
Committee and was Technical Secretary of the 1994 edition of Eurocode 5.
He is co-author of *Green oak in construction*, published by TRADA in 2007.

Giles Downes CVO, RIBA
Senior Partner at Sidell Gibson Architects, where he was responsible for
new design in the reconstruction of Windsor Castle. He has been Chairman
of the Judges for the annual Wood Awards for the last seven years, and is
a Warden of the Carpenters' Company; and Governor of the Building Crafts
College. He is also a member of the Institute of Wood Science, and of the
Fabric Committee at the Royal Albert Hall..

Andrew Lawrence MA (Cantab), PGCDMM, CEng,
MICE, MIStructE
A member of the BSI's UK Timber Code Committee and the leading timber
specialist at Arup, where he is an Associate, working for Arup Technology
and Research. His timber projects include the 2005 Serpentine Pavilion in
London and the Metz Pompidou in north-east France. He has received the
Pai Lin Li Travel Award and the Guthrie Brown Award from the Institution of
Structural Engineers for his work in the field of timber bridges. He was also
awarded the Baker Prize by Cambridge University.

The publisher and authors acknowledge with thanks:
Patrick Hislop of TRADA Technology for his assistance in the joinery and
cladding sections.
Maritz Vandenberg for co-ordinating and editing this project, and for his
work on the drawings.

Introduction

It is now some twenty-five years since the Timber Research and Development Association published *Timber in construction*, which was probably the first publication to look comprehensively at the role of timber in the building industry.

In TRADA's seventy-fifth anniversary year, it is appropriate to revisit the subject with a completely new text, prompted by the many technical developments in the intervening years. These have both extended the range of materials and widened the variety of forms available to the designer. The dominant issue today, however, is surely the growing awareness of the interaction between the environment and our way of life, and the role which timber can play in sustainable construction.

The authors' aim has been to act as a guide to readers who are interested in the field of timber in building construction, but have no special knowledge of the subject, using a step-by-step approach:

- CHAPTER 1: THE APPEAL OF TIMBER identifies the unique properties which make the material popular with designers, such as its visual and tactile qualities, and its environmental credentials. The next three chapters follow a design path for a timber project.

- CHAPTER 2: THE MATERIALS OF CONSTRUCTION considers the range of timber-based products which are available to the designer and their properties in relation to strength, movement and durability. It also summarises the issues relating to sustainability and certification.

- CHAPTER 3: CONNECTIONS reviews the ways in which one piece of timber can be connected to another, and the influence which the material properties have on the various joint forms. This chapter deliberately precedes design guidance on the members themselves, because joints are generally the more critical aspect of timber assemblies.

- CHAPTER 4: APPLICATIONS looks at the amazing variety of structural forms which are possible, and the manner in which they can be utilised to span space, as roofs, or to create whole building frames. The latter part of the chapter is devoted to window joinery, cladding and external structure, when exposure to rain makes issues of durability more significant.

- CHAPTER 5: INNOVATION identifies new processes or uses of timber, which include applications to structures seen traditionally as the preserve of concrete or steel.

The book concludes with a series of CASE STUDIES which have been chosen to illustrate the principles set out in the previous chapters, and because they are all exemplars in the use of timber.

Contents

5 Innovation   113

Case studies   124

Further reading   190

1

The appeal of timber

Peter Ross

Timber is a material with a unique charisma – it was,
after all, once living, and its organic origins are clear in its
appearance and texture. It also has an historic resonance,
since a thousand-year tradition is still evident in the great
frames and roofs of the medieval period and earlier.
Overall, its appeal to designers is based principally on its:

- Visual and tactile qualities

- Material properties

- Environmental credentials.

Sheffield Winter Garden.
Photo: Buro Happold

Figure 1.01 *(right)*
Birch veneer.
Photo: TRADA Technology

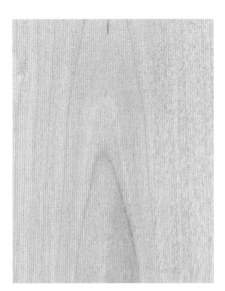

Figure 1.02 *(far right)*
Solid planks of African walnut, as doors for built-in furniture. Private flat, London.
Architect: McDowell+ Benedetti architects

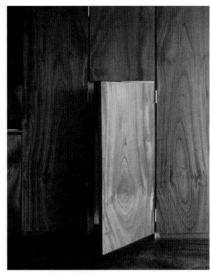

1.1 Visual and tactile qualities

The appearance of timber, in terms of its colour range and surface texture, is probably the primary reason for its use in both carpentry and joinery. The colour can vary from the light cream of birch *(Figure 1.01)*, to the regal depths of African walnut *(Figure 1.02)*, with many intermediate shades.

But the appeal lies not in the colour alone (since any particular shade can be replicated with paint) but in the organic lines of the surface figure, created as the geometric plane of the saw-cut intersects the naturally formed growth rings of the trunk. The figure may be further enlivened by knots, which of course mark the branch positions on the original truck. Thus, strictly, each piece can be considered unique. It is these inherent small variations between planks which give a liveliness to the surface of an assembly, such as panelling or cladding *(Figure 1.05)*.

The long traditions of the carpenter and joiner testify that timber is the most easily worked of the construction materials, and that its appearance can also be influenced by the method of conversion from the log. At its simplest, cleft timber is formed by splitting the log with a blade which follows the grain, a technique most often used for fence rails *(Figure 1.04)*. The results are rarely straight, but form members which are exceptionally strong and resilient. The use of an adze results in a surface with shallow scallop-like depressions *(Figure 1.05)*.

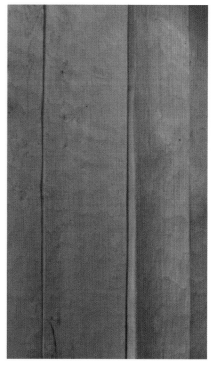

Figure 1.03 *(left)*
The texture of cladding in western red cedar, compared to the uniformity of aluminium.
Arup campus, Birmingham.
***Architect:** Arup Associates*

Figure 1.04
Fence rails in cleft timber.

Figure 1.05
Adzed panels in Sutton Hoo Museum.
***Architect:** van Heyningen and Haward Architects*

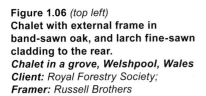

Figure 1.06 *(top left)*
Chalet with external frame in band-sawn oak, and larch fine-sawn cladding to the rear.
Chalet in a grove, Welshpool, Wales
Client: Royal Forestry Society;
Framer: Russell Brothers

Figure 1.07 *(right)*
Poppyhead stall end.
Southwold Church, Suffolk.

Figure 1.08 *(above)*
Staircase newel in the Globe Theatre, London. Polish is entirely due to hand contact.
Architect: Pentagram

Band sawing produces a characteristic marking on the face *(Figure 1.06)*, while fine sawing is only discernible on close inspection. All conversion marks can be removed by planing, which nevertheless shows the figure most clearly, and is the most user-friendly surface in areas of frequent hand-contact. Wood is also an excellent medium for carving *(Figure 1.07)* although, unlike free-stone, the material has a grain, and the carver must respect this.

With all these inherent qualities, wood needs little in the way of applied finishes. It is possible to use none, and allow a patina to develop simply by the conditions of use *(Figure 1.08)*. Finely polished timber almost demands hand contact, as instanced by the 'please do not touch' notices found on furniture in stately homes. But for more utilitarian uses there are of course a large range of paints and stains which can be used in traditional or modern ways, and which can allow the underlying texture to be seen *(Figure 1.09)*.

While the most charismatic species are largely confined by their price to joinery work, there are many softwood timbers such as redwood, Douglas fir *(Figure 1.10)* and Western red cedar, or hardwoods such as oak or chestnut which have handsome and distinctive figures.

Figure 1.09a *(top)*
Instantly recognisable painted panels at the RSPB Environment and Education Centre, Rainham Marshes.
Architect: *van Heyningen and Haward Architects*

Figure 1.09b *(above)*
Detail of the panels at the RSPB Environment and Education Centre.

Figure 1.10 *(left)*
First floor structure in Douglas fir. Kindersley Conference Centre, Berkshire.
Architect: *Alec French*

Figure 1.12
The wonderfully 'over-the-top' roof of the Church of St John the Baptist, Bere Regis, Dorset.

Figure 1.11
Glulam arches in the Sheffield Winter Garden.
Architect: Pringle Richards Sharratt Architects;
Engineer: Buro Happold
Photo: Buro Happold

Figure 1.13 *(far right)*
Temple in Kyoto, Japan.

1.2 Material properties

The properties of timber can be traced back to its organic origin. Its cellular structure is strongly directional, which in turn generates linear members with a strength-to-weight ratio exceeding that of mild steel, and makes timber very appropriate for roof construction. The restriction which in the past limited individual members to the size of cut logs has been removed by the development of durable adhesives which allow individual laminates to be glued together, until their size is limited only by the constraints of transport *(Figure 1.11)*.

A vocabulary of connections between the members themselves has evolved, from traditional all-timber interlocks to modern fasteners of metal. Although the cellular structure of the material imposes a discipline on the design of the joint, the procedure is set out in modern design standards. There is also a visual satisfaction in seeing the logic of construction expressed in an assembled structure. No other building material has such a historic breadth of structural vocabulary, which can be seen across the world from Europe *(Figure 1.12,)* to the Far East *(Figure 1.13)*.

Combustibility, and the possibility of fungal decay, are sometimes seen as the downside of timber construction. Originating from the organic nature of timber, they are in reality issues of design which have established solutions in terms, for instance, of applied protection for fire resistance, or species choice in relation to durability. For much routine design work, these issues require no special consideration – roofs normally need no period of fire resistance, and all species can be regarded as durable within the weather envelope of the building. Later chapters of this book deal in more detail with the properties of timber and their application to design.

Figure 1.14
Haberdashers' Hall, London, with ceiling, roof structure, walls and floor in American white oak.
Client: Haberdashers' Livery Company;
Architect: Sir Michael Hopkins and Partners;
Engineer: Arup

Unprotected timber on the external face of the building also undergoes a colour change, but this should be regarded as a material characteristic, rather than a defect, which for well-detailed assemblies can enhance the appearance. Later chapters of this book deal in more detail with the properties of timber in relation to all these issues.

1.3 Environmental credentials

In little more than a generation, concerns relating to the environment, such as the greenhouse effect and the finite nature of our resources in relation to a burgeoning world population, have moved from an unthought idea, to discussion and debate, and then (in many cases) to legislation which attempts to limit the consequences of global warming.

Timber, in these terms, is a very 'green' material. If forests were suitably husbanded, supplies could be maintained indefinitely for minimal carbon emissions, and the purpose of the various certification schemes is to ensure this.

Currently, as noted in *Section 2.2.2*, the world's softwood forests are actually increasing in area. Thus timber has the lowest carbon emissions, forest-to-site, of the major building materials. In addition, timber in a building effectively sequesters carbon, rather than releasing it to the atmosphere. For these reasons, timber scores highly in the various environmental assessments now required for any new building.

Figure 1.15
Redwood chalet in a grove,
Welshpool, Wales *(see figure 1.06).*
Cedar shingle roof, redwood framing
and oak cladding.
Client: *Royal Forestry Society;*
Framer: *Russell Brothers*

1.4 Conclusion

Thus the appeal of timber, in terms of its appearance and properties, is matched by a great versatility of application. The illustrations above have shown it used for cladding, structural framing and interior finishes. When used in combination, the strong character of the material will give unity to the design *(Figure 1.14)*. And in a landscaped setting, no other material can have such a close relationship to its surroundings *(Figure 1.15)*.

It is, however, true that timber stands a little apart from the inorganic building materials, and so designers are perhaps less familiar with its properties and vocabulary of form. The aim of this book is to provide design guidance and examples of good practice which demonstrate timber's potential in the field of contemporary construction.

2
The materials of construction
Andrew Lawrence

Three hundred million years of evolution have generated a wealth of timber species with a vast range of appearance, strength and resistance to decay. Relatively recent developments of timber composites and board materials also mean that the designer is no longer limited to the size of timber that can be cut from the log. This chapter examines the range of timber-based products available and discusses the increasingly important issues of sustainability and certification.

2.1 The general characteristics of timber

2.1.1 Strength and structure

Cellular material

Timber is an anisotropic material, having different properties in different directions. It is therefore very unlike the metals, to which most designers are accustomed. J.E.Gordon in *The New Science of Strong Materials* likens the trunk of a tree to a bundle of drinking straws *(Figure 2.01)* – cells mainly running parallel to the trunk to support the weight of the tree and to convey the sap up to the leaves. Just as a bundle of straws is stronger along its length, so timber is five to ten times stronger parallel to the cells or grain than perpendicular. As a result of the anisotropic nature of timber, the relief of stresses caused by differential shrinkage can easily lead to the development of fissures.

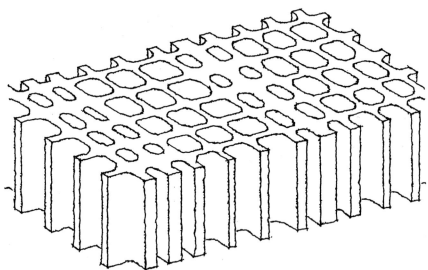

Growth depends on environmental conditions. In temperate climates, following the dormant winter season, the *earlywood* of the softwoods is characterised by relatively rapid growth – with thinner walled cells and a more open texture than the *latewood*. This annual cycle produces a distinctive pattern of growth rings which can be seen most clearly in a transverse section *(Figure 2.02)*. In tropical areas, growth is more or less continuous, but seasonal variations in rainfall may produce a similar, although less pronounced, effect.

Strength and density

All timber, from whatever species, has the same basic constituents – cellulose, hemi-cellulose and lignin. The main variation between species is the density or packing of the cells. For a 'small clear', free of defects such as knots, there is therefore a reasonably good correlation between density and strength/stiffness, independent of species. Softwoods for example generally have a lower density and therefore lower strength than many of the hardwoods. However, not all hardwoods are stronger (Balsa for example is

Figure 2.01 *(right)*
Cellular structure of softwood showing the bands of denser latewood.
Drawing: Arup

Figure 2.02 *(top and above)*
Christmas tree showing the taper of the trunk and the annular growth rings.

classed as a hardwood). This is because the terms softwood and hardwood actually refer to the botanical origin of the timbers rather than their physical properties – see *Section 2.2.1. Table 2.1* compares the densities of some common species.

The effect of natural defects

The bending strength at failure of a small piece of timber, free of knots and perfectly aligned with the grain can, in the densest species, be as high as 180 N/mm^2 (compare 275 N/mm^2 for mild steel). However, in design we use much lower values to provide an adequate factor of safety against brittle failure as well as to account for the effect of natural defects.

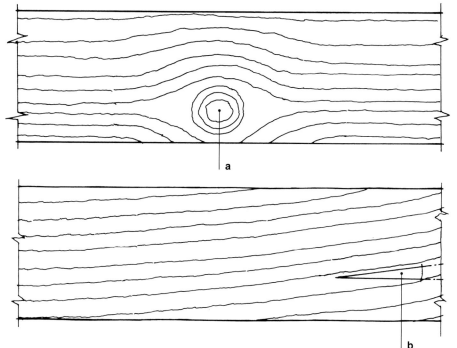

a

b

Figure 2.03
The most important natural defects affecting strength are:

a knots and

b slope of grain.

Drawing: Arup

The most important defects are knots and slope of grain *(Figure 2.03)*. Knots are the remains of branches, enclosed by the growth of the stem as it increases in diameter. Knots disturb the line of the grain, rather as if there were a hole cut through the timber. A knot cutting through the highly stressed outer tension fibres will cause a significant reduction in the bending strength. Slope of grain results from cutting a straight member from a bowed trunk, or from a straight trunk with spiral grain, and leads to a strength reduction because of the lower strength of the timber perpendicular to the grain. This effect was obviated in medieval cruck frames *(Figure 2.04)* where the timber was cut from a curved trunk, which followed the line of the grain.

Creep

The trunk of a tree is predominantly in compression, but it has evolved to resist high short-term bending loads generated by the wind. In the same way, a timber beam is stronger and stiffer under shorter term loads such as snow or wind, whereas under sustained loads it will not only tend to creep (leading to about 60% additional deflection for seasoned timber, and even more for green timber), but will also be up to 40% weaker. The physical

Figure 2.04
A surviving medieval cruck frame at Weobley, Herefordshire.
Photo: Andrew Lawrence

Figure 2.05 *(top)*
While all timber creeps under load, the effect is more pronounced in composite boards such as chipboard.

Figure 2.07 *(above)*
Non-uniform shrinkage can sometimes lead to deep fissures, particularly in larger sections containing the boxed heart of the log.
Photo: Andrew Lawrence

reasons for this behaviour are complex and partly related to sliding between the cell fibres.

The effect is more pronounced in composite board materials, such as chipboard *(Figure 2.05)*. The creep occurs within the adhesive used to glue the woodchips together, and the large proportion of adhesive in chipboard means that the effect is considerably more pronounced than in solid timber shelves, in which the proportion of natural adhesives (lignin) is rather lower.

2.1.2 Movement and shrinkage

Drying shrinkage
Not only is timber weaker across the grain, but it also tends to shrink and swell with varying moisture content. A living tree contains a considerable amount of water, held partly as sap within the cell cavities and partly bound into the cell walls. After cutting, water is lost first from the cavities and then from the walls. As the walls dry they shrink in diameter, leading to tangential shrinkage across the grain. Shrinkage parallel to the grain is almost entirely restrained by the cell fibres. A small number of radial cells also help to reduce the radial shrinkage to about half the tangential value.

This non-uniform shrinkage can cause distortion on drying *(Figure 2.06)*: the distortion of the square piece into a diamond demonstrates the different rates of radial and tangential shrinkage; floor boards which are quarter- or rift-sawn (as X or Y in *Figure 2.06*) will stay flatter than boards which are plain-sawn (Z). As an aid to predicting the distortion, imagine that as a piece dries the growth rings tend to straighten out. The non-uniform shrinkage can sometimes lead to deep fissures, particularly in larger sections containing the boxed heart of the tree *(Figure 2.07)*. However, the only case in which drying fissures will occur through the full depth of the piece (when they are known as splits) is at each end – due to the more rapid loss of moisture from the end-grain, then from the lateral surfaces.

To limit shrinkage after installation, we try to specify dry timber, with a moisture content as close as possible to the in-service moisture content. Moisture content is defined as the weight of the contained water divided by the weight of the dry timber, and can vary from 8-12% in an internal heated environment to 16-18% at an external well ventilated location. In the past, timber was left to dry naturally. This process, called seasoning, could take several months or years depending on the species and the thickness of the piece. Today, most softwood is kiln-dried in a matter of days or weeks *(Figure 2.08)*. Hardwoods are generally denser and can take considerably longer to dry, to the point where this dominates the cost of the timber. Thus green or unseasoned oak might cost only 30-50% of seasoned material. Depending on species, timber over 75-100mm in thickness cannot be effectively kiln-dried.

Seasonal movement
Shrinkage is partly reversible, so that timbers will tend to swell across the grain in humid winter conditions and shrink back in the summer. This effect, called seasonal movement, can cause the timber to shrink or swell by 1% or so, depending on species and location (movements for common

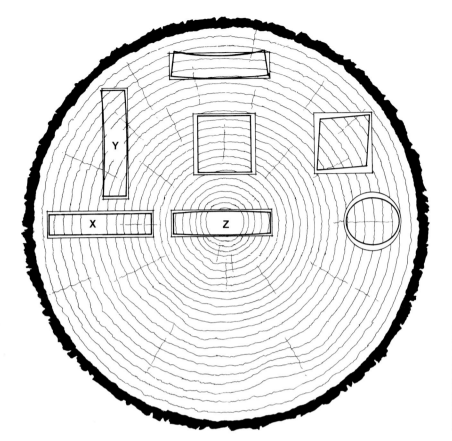

Figure 2.06
Non-uniform radial and tangential shrinkage leads to distortion on drying.
Drawing: Arup

Figure 2.08
During kiln drying the timber is 'sticked and stacked' to promote air circulation and drying.
Photo: Andrew Lawrence

species are included in *Table 2.1*). Though small, this is enough to cause doors to stick or large glued members to fissure *(Figure 2.09)*, because the outside of the member dries and shrinks before the core. Thus for exterior joinery, say, it is helpful to select a small movement timber to reduce the risk of fissuring and prolong the life of the finishes. In order to allow for movement in a solid timber floor, regular or edge expansion gaps should be provided.

In passing, it should be noted that the coefficient of thermal expansion of timber parallel to the grain is only one third that of steel or concrete, and is generally ignored, particularly as it is partly counterbalanced by moisture movement of the timber.

2.1.3 Resistance to decay

The risk of fungal decay and insect attack

In temperate climates, insect attack of timber inside a building is generally not a significant risk and fungal decay (rot) can only occur in wet timber where the moisture content exceeds about 20%. Even outside, so long as the timber is under cover, the moisture content will not exceed about 16%, so wet rot can only occur where the timber is exposed to rain or condensation, or where it is in contact with wet ground. Dry rot can admittedly be more of a problem – although it can only take hold on wet timber, it is then able to conduct its own water through mycelial plant-like shoots to other, drier, parts of the structure. Very limited areas of the UK, as identified in the Building Regulations, are also at risk from House Longhorn Beetle.

Figure 2.09
Seasonal moisture movements can lead to fissuring of large glulam members.
Photo: Andrew Lawrence

Figure 2.10a (below)
Park bench made from oak heartwood.

Figure 2.10b (left inset)
Detail of end of arm rest. After 20 years service, the vulnerable end grain has started to decay.

Figure 2.11 *(above)*
The end of this timber at Cranbrook Church in Kent decayed because it was built into a damp external wall.
Photo: Andrew Lawrence

Figure 2.12 *(left)*
Timber can offer a very durable option in a pool environment, because the timber moisture content is safely below the threshold for decay.
Photo: Andrew Lawrence

Timbers liable to remain wet for long periods are the most prone to decay. Outside, this might imply shaded horizontal surfaces or timber that has been bedded into the ground, rather than raised up on a plinth. The exposed end-grain, which can soak up water like a straw, stays wet longer and is always particularly vulnerable. Even a durable timber such as European or American white oak *(Figure 2.10)* will eventually decay, given a prolonged moisture content over 20%. Inside a building, the most common causes of rot are leaking roofs, particularly where there is poor ventilation or where the timbers are built into a damp external wall *(Figure 2.11)*. So long as these risks are avoided any species of timber can be used inside the weather envelope without risk of decay. Even in a swimming pool environment, for example, the normal combination of temperature and humidity will ensure that the moisture content of the timber never exceeds about 16%, making timber a more durable option than steel or concrete in this potentially corrosive environment *(Figure 2.12)*.

Figure 2.13
The heartwood of European oak contains natural toxins which protect it against decay. Note how the wood-destroying fungi have only attacked the sapwood.
Photo: Andrew Lawrence

Figure 2.14
Stake tests are used to determine the durability against fungal attack at the vulnerable ground/air interface. The stakes are tested at intervals to check their residual strength.
Photo: BRE

Natural durability

For timber, the term 'durability' usually denotes inherent resistance to fungal or insect attack (although in the USA, durability is used to mean hardwearing).

The trunk of a tree consists of a central core of heartwood, surrounded by the sapwood (which unlike the heartwood still serves the role of conduction and storage) and finally the thin living cambium just below the bark. The heartwood accumulates extractives, which in many species leaves it darker than the sapwood *(Figure 2.07)*. The extractives are sometimes toxic, giving the timber a natural resistance to decay. In practice few timbers native to cold or temperate climates have significant natural durability. The most notable exceptions are European oak *(Figure 2.13)* and American white oak, which explains why European oak is found in many of the surviving European medieval frames *(Figure 2.04)*. When using a naturally durable timber, it is obviously important to specify that the sapwood is excluded since this contains no extractives and therefore has no natural durability.

Resistance to fungal attack for common species has been measured by stake tests of 50 mm square posts driven into the ground *(Figure 2.14)*. The timber near the ground surface, where there is an adequate supply of both water from the ground and oxygen from the air is particularly vulnerable to decay, making this a relatively onerous test. The durability of most of the common species is given in EN 350 (which defines five durability classes), and a selection of these are included in *Table 2.1*. Durability can vary depending upon where, and how fast, a timber is grown. For example UK grown Western red cedar or Douglas fir tends to be less durable than the same timber grown in Canada.

Rather than using a naturally durable timber, it is possible with certain limitations to add artificial toxins called preservatives, and this is discussed in more detail in *Section 2.6*. However, the weathered appearance of preserved timber is generally less attractive than that of untreated naturally durable timbers.

It is also possible to make timber more durable by chemical modification – see *Section 2.3.7*.

Detailing for durability

Where there is a risk of decay, then as well as using a naturally durable or preserved timber, measures to limit the uptake of water and promote rapid drying will prolong the life of a member. Such measures might include:

- Roof overhangs to shield vertical surfaces from the rain, although this may result in an uneven appearance of timber without finishes, due to the varying exposure to sun and rain *(Figure 2.15)*. Similarly doors and windows should be set back from the face of the building.

- Lifting the timber a good 200-250 mm off the ground to prevent 'splashback' *(Figure 2.16)* for instance by mounting the columns on steel brackets.

- Protecting exposed end-grain on beams and posts with an end-grain sealer, or a sacrificial timber or metal cap *(Figure 2.17)*.

- Providing a slight slope to horizontal surfaces to promote run off, especially away from joints where water might become trapped. For wide horizontal surfaces a metal cap should be provided, with an air gap under the cap for ventilation *(Figure 2.18)*, to prevent the risk of fissuring. For decking, boards should ideally be laid heartside up to ensure any cupping (which might otherwise trap water) is limited to the underside.

- Avoiding water traps.

- Providing drip grooves on the underside of members and anti-capillary grooves between close surfaces to prevent water being drawn in by capillary action.

- By providing good ventilation to promote drying, especially where there is a risk of condensation such as in roof spaces and floor voids or behind cladding *(Figure 2.19)*. A common mistake when adding roof insulation is to completely surround the rafters with insulation and to seal up the soffit board air vents, thus preventing any unwanted rainwater (due perhaps to a slipped tile) from evaporating. Air spaces should always be ventilated to the outside, to avoid the risk of condensation of the vapour within the humid internal air.

Regular inspection and maintenance will also help identify areas where water might be accumulating, so that remedial measures can be taken. Overall, the message is keep the timber dry and it will offer an almost indefinite life.

2.2 Selecting a suitable species

2.2.1 Commonly used species and their properties

Trees can be divided into three distinct families:

- The softwoods or conifers such as pine and spruce, which chiefly grow in Northern Europe, the Northern United States and Canada, and represent about half the world's forests.

Figure 2.15 *(top)*
The overhang shields the façade from sun and rain, preserving the original colour of the angelim cladding. This picture was taken after only three years; the remainder of the façade will eventually turn grey.
Photo: Andrew Lawrence

Figure 2.16 *(above)*
Note how the medieval oak frame of Little Morton Hall has been lifted well clear of the ground to protect it from 'splash-back' and rising damp.
Photo: Andrew Lawrence

Figure 2.17 *(top left)*
The end grain of the parapet posts on this bridge in New York State has been protected with plastic caps.
Photo: Andrew Lawrence

Figure 2.18
Copper caps are used to protect
the upper surfaces of the arches
on this bridge in Norway.
Photo: *Andrew Lawrence*

- The temperate hardwoods of Europe and North America (as well as parts of Russia and Asia), such as oak and beech.

- The diverse family of tropical hardwoods native to the rainforests. This includes the eucalypts, native to Australia, but now grown widely in Asia, South Africa and South America as a forestry timber.

The terms softwood and hardwood refer to the botanical origin of the timbers rather than their physical properties. Softwoods have needle shaped leaves (which have developed to help reduce the wind loads in the windier northern climates in which they tend to grow) and naked seeds, whereas hardwoods have broad leaves, with seeds enclosed in a seed case.

The three families of timber are discussed in general terms below. A more detailed comparison of the main species is included in *Table 2.1*.

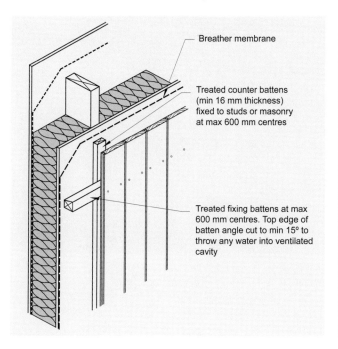

Breather membrane

Treated counter battens (min 16 mm thickness) fixed to studs or masonry at max 600 mm centres

Treated fixing battens at max 600 mm centres. Top edge of batten angle cut to min 15° to throw any water into ventilated cavity

The softwoods

Nearly all the timber used for structural purposes is softwood. In the UK, this is principally spruce (as well as some pine) from Scandinavia, Eastern Europe and Russia. Some UK grown timber is available (again mainly spruce), but the quantity is limited and the density and thus strength tends to be lower than imported softwood thanks to the more favourable UK climate and thus longer growing season.

Softwood is generally pale and instantly recognisable from the regular pattern of knots (*Figure 2.20*), which are remains of the numerous thin side branches. The softwoods or conifers, as they are often called, grow fast and straight (*Figure 2.21*), making them relatively cheap and also efficient for cutting into long beams, without excessive wastage. Although of only modest strength compared to many hardwoods thanks to their low density and frequent knots, they are adequate for most loadbearing applications.

Figure 2.19 *(left)*
The ventilated cavity behind timber cladding helps to ensure rapid drying of the timber after rainfall.

Figure 2.20 *(above)*
Softwood is instantly recognisable from the regular pattern of knots, here made more prominent after years of wear.
***Photo:** Andrew Lawrence*

Larch (typically from Southern Germany or Siberia) and Douglas fir (typically from Canada) are sometimes used, instead of spruce, for their improved resistance to decay. Being moderately durable, they are suitable for cladding and other locations with only intermittent wetting, but where the water is free to run off allowing the timber to dry fairly rapidly. Western red cedar is more resistant to decay, being classed as durable, but only has adequate strength for cladding and joinery applications *(Figure 2.22)*. Scots pine is also used externally – while having little inherent durability, it is more permeable than spruce making it easier to pressure-impregnate with preservative.

Figure 2.21 *(right)*
A typical Finnish forest of European redwood.
Photo: Andrew Lawrence

Figure 2.22 *(above)*
The vertical fins at the Agora newspaper headquarters in Warsaw are laminated from Western red cedar.

The temperate hardwoods

The temperate hardwoods or deciduous trees of Europe and North America, such as oak, maple, beech and walnut, show much more variation between species, but are generally darker, denser and stronger than the softwoods. They are often beautifully figured and are prized for joinery work. This, combined with the additional forest management (required to encourage straight trunks and remove side branches), slower growth rates and the longer kilning times (necessitated by the denser timber), can make them several times more expensive than the softwoods. Correspondingly, they find more applications in joinery and furniture than carpentry, although European and American white oak (and when available, chestnut) are sometimes used in loadbearing applications (such as footbridges, lock gates, decking and high profile architectural work) for the combination of its strength, figure and natural resistance to decay. However, most temperate hardwoods have little or no natural durability and are not suitable for exterior use.

The tropical hardwoods

The tropical hardwoods are a very diverse grouping. They are generally denser and darker than the softwoods, and some such as teak have a very beautiful figure as well as a fine grain, making them ideal for high quality joinery. In consequence they have generally been priced out of the structural market, being mainly used for decking, cladding and furniture. However, they include some of the strongest and most durable of the timbers, which are used for bridges and marine structures (usually greenheart), where their good resistance to decay enables them to achieve the required design life.

2.2.2 Sustainability issues

Timber is our only truly renewable construction material and because it grows using solar energy it also has the lowest embodied energy – even the heat needed to dry the timber can be derived from burning the off-cut waste, bark and branches. Forests also soak up carbon dioxide from the atmosphere, so that if a forest is harvested and replanted, the carbon dioxide locked into the felled timber will result in a small reduction in the levels of carbon dioxide in the atmosphere.

While the loss of the tropical rainforests has focused attention on the sustainability of timber as a resource, it should be remembered that most timber used in construction is sourced from well managed softwood plantations in Europe and North America.

The potential impacts of timber production

Deforestation and illegal logging
Obviously we can only call timber a renewable material if the forest is felled no faster than it can re-grow – referred to as the sustainable yield. In Northern Europe and North America, the area of softwood and temperate hardwood forest is actually increasing in response to timber demand as well as tight forestry laws. By comparison, the rainforests are being rapidly depleted, mainly due to clearance for agriculture (for food, biofuels, palm oil, rubber etc), but also in part due to logging. While the logging industry itself is small, the logging roads open up the forests to other development. Sometimes this clearance is legal; sometimes it is illegal, but many governments do not have the resources to prevent it.

Loss of old-growth forest
Again, this is more relevant to the tropical rainforests, since most of our softwood and temperate hardwood is now derived from plantations in Europe and North America. However, some old-growth softwood forest does remain, particularly in North America and Russia, and views differ over the extent to which these should be conserved. Non-governmental organizations argue that they should not be touched, citing the loss of diversity when they are turned into plantations. Local communities and public bodies often disagree, pointing out that they are more or less single species plantations and that clearance (by forest fire) was always a natural part of the forest cycle, providing the light that the seedlings needed to grow. After local clearance it is common for softwood forests in Switzerland *(Figure 2.23)*, Scandinavia and elsewhere, to be left to seed naturally, leaving a far more natural appearance with a degree of mixed species (typically a mix of softwoods combined with birch, which is often a pioneer species after clearance), compared to parallel rows of planted trees.

Figure 2.23
Many of Switzerland's hillsides are actively managed to provide timber for construction and joinery. This mixed spruce and larch plantation above Chur is PEFC certified.
Photo: Andrew Lawrence

Loss of diversity

Felling a mixed species old-growth forest and replacing it with a single species plantation would bring an obvious loss in diversity, particularly as plantations usually require chemical treatment of the competing vegetation in their early rotation. Increasingly, mixed species plantations are being used in an attempt to match the diversity of the original ecosystem.

Impact on the local economy

In its broadest sense sustainability also embraces sustainable economics. For example, ceasing to use certain tropical hardwoods to try and prevent destruction of the rainforests (as was advocated in the early 90s) would disadvantage those people who relied on forestry for their livelihoods and might even encourage replacement of the trees with a more profitable cash crop. Before criticising too strongly we should remember that this is exactly what our forbears did 1000 years ago in Europe and 300 years ago in North America, and is what now enables us to be more or less self-sufficient in terms of food production.

Options for the specifier

Building requires resources, and use of those resources will always have some impact on the environment. The advantage of timber is that with careful specification of timber from well managed forests we can help to minimise that impact.

Careful choice of species

Careful choice of species is the biggest single factor in determining the sustainability of supply. As can be seen from the above discussions, the softwoods and temperate hardwoods are much more likely to have been legally and sustainably grown than the tropical hardwoods.

Specifying certified timber

The concept of timber certification has developed as a means to offer specifiers some control over the source of the timber used on a project, however remote that source might be. There are two sides to certification: (a) independent verification that the timber has been felled legally (i.e. in accordance with local forest laws) and at a sustainable rate, combined with (b) a robust chain of custody to ensure that the timber remains segregated so that it can be tracked from forest, through sawmill and other processing to the end user.

This may sound straightforward, but the reality is rather more complex:

- Since there is no universally agreed definition of sustainability, the criteria against which the forests are measured can vary significantly between different certification schemes *(Figure 2.24)*. Those schemes which are more independent of the forest owners, such as the Forest Stewardship Council (FSC), will tend to take a broader view of sustainability, including impact on the local environment and communities (e.g. ensuring a fair wage *(Figure 2.25)*, and they also place more emphasis on continuous improvement. To address the differences between the various certification schemes, the UK Government has established the Central Point of Expertise on Timber (CPET), which continuously reviews and compares each scheme for its ability to provide both legal and sustainable supplies of timber. While this is principally intended to help specifiers of timber for public projects, the results are freely available and will be of benefit to all specifiers.

- Adoption of a particular certification scheme tends to be geographic. Nearly all softwood and temperate hardwood forests are now certified. But whereas all Forestry Commission forest in the UK is now FSC certified, the vast majority of Continental European and Scandinavian forests (from where most UK timber, including all our glulam are derived) are PEFC certified *(Figure 2.23)* (PEFC is the Programme for the Endorsement of Forest Certification schemes).

- If we accept that the biggest problem was always ensuring legal and sustainable supplies of tropical hardwoods, the bad news is that relatively little certified tropical hardwood is available. The reason is threefold. Firstly, and in some countries, there is still much illegal and indiscriminate felling. Secondly, the independent checks required to obtain certification are expensive to undertake - for a small privately owned forest in Africa these can easily add 10% or more to the cost of the sawn timber, but with little prospect of increased revenues. And thirdly, it is much more expensive to certify an area of natural forest (in which sustainable management requires selected- rather than clear-felling of a limited number of older trees, at a rate at which they can be replenished by natural re-growth) than a plantation. This explains why most

Figure 2.24
FSC and PEFC are two of the most common certification schemes, particularly within Europe.

FSC certified tropical hardwood comes from plantations (typically in Brazil and South Africa), whereas it is still impossible to obtain certified supplies of for example greenheart (the best timber for use in marine environments), despite the fact that Guyana has invested huge resources in recording the age and location of trees in her forests and has a long established programme of selective felling. Part of the reason that all UK Forestry Commission forest is certified, is that it was relatively easy to certify large areas of single species plantation in common ownership and already under good management.

- Because certified tropical timbers are often fast grown in plantations away from their native habitat, there is rarely any reliable strength and durability data available. A conservative estimate of strength can usually be made based on limited testing where available, but durability can only be approximated by comparative laboratory tests.

Figure 2.25
Requirements of FSC certification for this Eucalyptus forest near Durban, South Africa, included leaving local areas near rivers fallow to protect the lpcal ecosystem and fair wages for the foresters.
Photo: Andrew Lawrence

The North American hardwood industry has recently published a study showing that there is less than a 1% risk of illegal hardwood entering the commercial chain. This has been applauded by some NGO's as a way forward for establishing legality.

Specifying locally grown timber

Increasingly, specifiers are requesting locally grown timber to limit energy in transport – in timber, the main component of the embodied energy. While this makes sense in principle, it is important to ensure that the timber specified is actually available locally. Most UK forestry timber is fast-grown spruce. Though less strong than slower grown spruce from colder climates, this would certainly be adequate for interior carpentry and low rise structural applications, but the spruce glulam required for larger structures is only manufactured abroad, close to the supply of the slower grown denser raw material. Other species such as oak, larch or Western red cedar may occasionally be available locally, but these will be in very small quantities and generally in smaller section sizes. Experience shows that the UK grown larch, Douglas fir and Western red cedar are generally less strong and less durable than imported material from colder climates.

The definition of local is also important – for a project in say the South East of England there may not be a significant difference in the energy in transport between for example Scottish grown timber (transported by road) and Latvian timber (mainly transported by sea). In any event the embodied energy will certainly be considerably lower than alternative steel elements.

Avoiding over-specification

For joinery, specifying the highest grades which are effectively clear (i.e. knot free), will generally be a less sustainable option, since this either entails use of older growth trees which have lost their lower side branches, or generates significant wastage unless an alternative use can be found for the large proportion of the timber from a particular tree which will obviously not be knot free. For structural applications, where the members are rarely open to close scrutiny, specifiers should keep to the standard strength classes available, supplemented where necessary with local making good of defects as discussed in *Section 2.3.2*.

Specifying reused timber

While reused timber can offer a more sustainable option in theory (avoiding disposal of what would otherwise be waste material), in practice it would be difficult to obtain sufficient material for a contract of any scale, and for the present, recycled timber is likely to remain a niche market for floorboards and other domestic elements, for refurbishment work.

Specifiers should also be aware that reused timber is likely to be more expensive than new because of the additional costs in careful dismantling and storage, as well as the possibility of contamination with preservatives, finishes and nails.

The environmental issues associated with adhesives

Brief mention should be made of the adhesives used in, for example, glulam production. While these are often derived from oil, they make up much less than 1% of the volume of the fabricated element and enable long and large cross-section members to be fabricated from small diameter fast-grown plantation timber. In this way the glues enable very large members up to 40m long or more to be fabricated from relatively small pieces, which can compete with steel in terms of spanning capability but entail far less energy in their manufacture. As ever, sustainability is always about relative impacts.

Similarly, although plywood and some other board materials use larger amounts of adhesive, this again needs to be weighed against the sustainability of the alternatives such as plastic or aluminium panels.

While wood adhesives are often formaldehyde based, formaldehyde release is only an issue during manufacture where it can be easily controlled.

Conclusions

In conclusion, it is recommended that specifiers use softwood or temperate hardwood wherever possible (eg: most structural applications) and that these are certified under one of the schemes recognised as offering legal and sustainable timber by the CPET. Where it is justified to use tropical hardwood (in exterior applications such as decking *(Figure 2.26)* where its strength, density and durability can be of most value) it is suggested that this is either (a) FSC certified (in which case specifiers should be aware that supplies and species may be limited and therefore allow adequate lead times of at least 6-9 months for larger quantities as well as some flexibility over exact choice of species) or (b) carefully sourced from countries such as Ghana or Guyana with good records of sustainable forest management. Before specifying a hardwood, particularly a tropical hardwood, it is always important to speak to suppliers to check exactly what is available and, where certified timber is not available, what alternative guarantees they can offer that the timber has been sustainably sourced.

Figure 2.26
Vitex was selected for the decking at Chiswick Park, London, because it is available with FSC certification.
Architect: Rogers Stirk Harbour & Partners

2.3 The range of timber products available

Timber was originally limited to the size that could be cut from a log. However, relatively recent developments in processing and adhesive technologies have provided ways to slice, peel or chip the timber and then glue it back together to form larger members or panels for a wide range of applications. It is useful to understand the methods of conversion and manufacture, since these will generally determine the properties and appearance of the finished products, as well as the size limitations.

2.3.1 Solid timber

Size

Softwood

The majority of timber used for construction in the UK is softwood. The trees only grow to a modest size and the dimensions of sawn softwood (kiln-dried to below 20% moisture content) is therefore limited by the 300-600 mm diameter and the taper of a typical log *(Figure 2.02)*. The largest pieces generally available are about 6 m long and 225 mm wide. Larger sizes of (Canadian) Douglas fir can be obtained, perhaps up to 300 or 400 mm square, but only in limited quantities and these are still green. For kiln-dried timber, the maximum economic thickness is about 75 mm – thicker pieces cannot be dried effectively and would in any case split or fissure in the process. Within these limitations, kiln-dried sawn timber is available to standard cross section dimensions, in about 25 mm increments. Before use the timber will generally need to be planed to finished sizes, reducing the overall dimension by about 5 mm, compared with the original rough sawn size.

For joinery, size is less of a problem, but it requires higher quality in terms of straightness and size/numbers of knots.

Hardwood
Hardwood is mainly used for joinery, flooring and furniture. Larger sizes for structural use will only be available to order and these necessarily green or unseasoned. Green timber can also be considerably cheaper because of the saving in time and energy required for kiln-drying of the denser hardwood species (but see caveats on use of green timber in *Section 2.1.2*).

Structural grades

To account for natural defects such as knots and slope of grain *(Figure 2.03)*, all structural timber has to be graded according to a codified set of grading rules – the more significant the defects, the lower the grade. Tests have been undertaken to determine the strength of a particular grade in a particular species. The test results have been codified, giving strength values which can be used with confidence by the engineer for the purposes of structural design.

Much grading is still done by eye (often now a computer eye) and is referred to as 'visual grading', based principally on the number and distribution of knots, the slope of grain and wane. The visual grading rules define the size, type and number of strength reducing characteristics allowed in each grade. Increasingly, for softwoods, machine grading is also used, relying on the bending stiffness of the timber as a measure of strength. This is more accurate than visual grading and can therefore be used to achieve higher strengths.

Since strength is related to moisture content, the timber must be graded under similar conditions (typically dried to below 20%) to those under which it will be used. Timber above 20% moisture content or thicker than 100mm is normally graded and installed wet, with appropriate modification factors used in the design to allow for the lower strength of the wet timber.

Softwood
For non-architectural applications inside the building envelope, it is usual to specify softwood by generic strength class, rather than by species and grade. EN 338 defines theoretical strength classes (as a function of strength and density), ranging from C14 to C50 where C denotes Conifer and 16 the ultimate or characteristic bending strength in N/mm^2. The most commonly available strength classes are C16 and C24. Higher strengths up to C30 or C35 can be justified by machine grading, but entail necessarily higher reject rates and therefore a potential cost premium. It is unwise to base a design on the highest values without checking availability.

Figure 2.27
The oak that was used for this library table has been quarter-sawn to bring out the pattern of radial cells known as rays.

Hardwood

Temperate hardwoods can be obtained in a high and a low grade, while only a single grade is defined for the tropical hardwoods. Depending on species these will correspond to a generic strength class from about D30 (e.g. oak) to D70 (some of the stronger tropical hardwoods). Here the D denotes deciduous and the number represents the characteristic bending strength. It can therefore be seen that the hardwoods are generally stronger than the softwoods, due to their higher density and fewer knots. Since most hardwood is destined for non-structural applications, the hardwood will usually be structurally graded to order.

Joinery grades

Detailed guidance on the specification of timber for appearance, mainly used in joinery, is given in *BS EN 942: Timber in joinery – general classification of timber quality.* This includes guidance on suitable species and (where necessary) preservative treatments, as well as the appearance of the visible surfaces of the finished component.

Before specifying it would be prudent to contact suppliers to determine the quality of timber generally available from a particular species. The temptation to over-specify in terms of, for instance, acceptable knot sizes should be avoided since this could lead to significant wastage of timber and expense for the client.

BS EN 942 defines five classes of timber in terms of allowable knot size, as well as the inclusion of shakes, resin and bark pockets, loose knots, discoloured sapwood, exposed pith, and beetle damage. Classes J40 and J50 are intended for general purpose joinery and could include knots up to 40 or 50 mm diameter respectively, whereas class J30 will require special selection of the timber and therefore command a cost premium. Classes J2 and J10 will command a significant cost premium (due to the high reject rates) and may only be available in limited species.

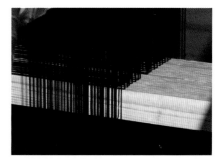

The type of finish for joinery will influence the class of timber required. For example, it may be acceptable for joinery which is to be covered with an opaque finish to have features which have been made good using plugs and fillers that would not be acceptable on a clear-finished product.

When the precise appearance of the timber is important to the finished project, the only totally reliable solution may be to inspect the timber prior to use or to request a sample for general approval. Where the specifier wishes the timber to be cut in a particular way to achieve a particular figure *(Figure 2.27)*, this will also need to be specified and samples obtained.

Exterior joinery will obviously require the selection of a suitably durable timber.

2.3.2 Glue laminated timber

Size

To make larger sections, dried softwood boards can be glued together to make glue laminated (glulam) beams. Individual laminates are finger jointed to the required length. Each laminate is then planed, run through a glue curtain, and stacked on its side with the other laminates in a clamping frame *(Figure 2.28)*. Inevitably, the additional costs associated with their manufacture increases the cost compared with the parent timber, but allows the timber to be used for larger projects.

The size of glulam is limited only by transport and the facilities of the particular manufacturer. Members up to 40m long by 2.5m deep have been produced *(Figure 2.29)* (this is discussed further in *Section 4.1.2)*. Standard cross-sections are available from stock up to about 500 x 200 mm. While it is common to fabricate specials for larger sections, widths above 220 mm or so will rarely be economic, since these will require more than one board to make up the width of any one layer. However, recent developments of water-

Figure 2.28
The steps in glulam manufacture.

a & b *(top left and middle)*
Fingerjointing;

c *(top right)*
Applying the adhesive with a glue curtain;

d & e *(bottom left and middle)*
Front and rear views of the racks used to clamp the timber together during the curing of the glue;

f *(bottom right)*
Planing.

Figure 2.29 *(right)*
The theoretical maximum size of a glulam beam is limited only by transport.
Photo: Andrew Lawrence

Figure 2.30 *(bottom right)*
Larger members can be fabricated by block-glueing several thinner beams together. This beam, for a roadbridge near Sneek in the Netherlands, will be fully exposed to the weather and has therefore been glued using phenol resorcinol formaldehyde, with its characteristic brown glue line.
Photo: Andrew Lawrence

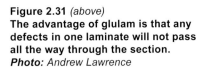

Figure 2.31 *(above)*
The advantage of glulam is that any defects in one laminate will not pass all the way through the section.
Photo: Andrew Lawrence

proof gap-filling adhesives that can tolerate lower pressures during curing have enabled massive glulam sections to be constructed by 'block glueing' several thinner glulam beams together *(Figure 2.30)*. Unlike the non-destructive testing of steel welds, there is as yet no way to check the strength of a glued timber joint without destructive testing. Thus very careful workmanship is required to ensure that the surfaces to be connected are adequately flat, that the glue is evenly spread, and that uniform pressure is applied during glueing.

In addition to producing members of almost any size, the laminates can easily be curved before glueing. This is discussed further in *Section 4.1.2*. 35-45mm thick laminates are typically used for structural members for economy and to minimise splitting, distortion and problems achieving adequate bond pressure. Thinner laminates will be required for tightly curved members. 19mm laminates are generally used for joinery.

Hardwood glulams are occasionally used where the requirements of strength, appearance, or durability demand. However, some hardwoods are more difficult to glue so careful consideration of species is required.

Strength

The great advantage of glulam is that any defects in one laminate will not pass all the way through the gross section *(Figure 2.31)*. This characteristic creates a member that is stronger than the laminates from which it is made. The increase in strength is obviously lower for higher grade (i.e. clearer) laminates which by definition contain fewer defects.

Glulam can be either 'homogenous', where all the laminates are the same strength class of timber or 'combined', where a higher grade timber is used for the more highly stressed outer laminates (one-sixth of the depth on both faces). Common European grades (defined in EN 1194) are GL28h and GL32c, where the number indicates the characteristic bending strength, and c/h denotes combined/homogeneous.

Since sawn softwood boards are limited to 5-6 m in length, they will need to be finger-jointed *(Figure 2.28b)* to suit the length of the glulam. Where high grade boards such as C30 or C35 are used for the laminates, the tensile strength of the finger-joints can start to dominate the strength of the member.

Moisture content

Since a moisture content below about 16% is required to ensure bonding of the adhesive, glulam beams tend to be drier than solid timber at time of installation, limiting subsequent shrinkage in an internal environment. However, large members are still prone to partial depth fissures, as the outside of the glulam dries and shrinks against the inside. The fissuring will be worse if the glulam is allowed to get wet during construction, and then rapidly dried by central heating before the inside has had time to dry out. Such fissures rarely affect the strength of the member, but might fall outside client expectations.

Adhesives

Adhesives are used in the finger-joints used to end-joint the laminates into long lengths *(Figure 2.28b)*, and also to bond the surface of one laminate to the next. The surfaces to be glued need to be flat, clean and dry, while an adequate pressure and temperature needs to be maintained until the adhesive has cured. For this reason glueing needs to be carried out under factory conditions and not on site, unless very tight controls are in place such as heating and a temporary roof. A properly glued joint should be stronger than the timber being connected.

Choice of adhesive depends chiefly on the required degree of water resistance and colour, as well as the conditions required for curing. For example a factory producing large quantities of straight glulam would favour a faster setting adhesive than a small specialist plant producing smaller quantities of bespoke curved members, which take longer to assemble but can also be left overnight.

Three adhesives are commonly used for glulam:-

- Phenol resorcinol formaldehyde (PRF) has a characteristic dark glue line *(Figure 2.30)*. It is the most water-resistant and is therefore the usual glue for external conditions.

- Inside the weather envelope, it is more common to find either Melamine Urea Formaldehyde (MUF) or Polyurethane (PU) based glues. They are not as water resistant as PRF but do have the advantage of being cheaper and colourless.

The formaldehydes have been in common use since the 1950's whereas polyurethanes have only been in use in the past ten years or so.

Epoxy resins are more forgiving in terms of the temperature and pressure required during curing, but are relatively expensive and therefore tend to be limited to repair work, where they are used because of their ability to bond timber to other materials such as steel and composites.

Compatibility of adhesives with flame retardants or preservatives should always be checked with the manufacturer. For example, preservatives which incorporate a water repellent, or flame retardants based on inorganic salts, will generally prevent the wood 'absorbing' the adhesive.

The environmental issues associated with adhesives are discussed in *Section 2.2.2.*

Appearance grades

For most glulam applications, it is usual to specify a planed surface free from glue stains, with exposed knot holes and fissures filled with glued inserts. Where close visual contact is possible, a better quality finish can be specified, at additional cost, with outer laminations carefully selected to match grain and colour at end joints where practicable, free from loose knots and open knot holes, and with reasonable care exercised in matching the direction of grain and colour of the glued inserts.

**Figure 2.32
Making good of a loose knot with glued inserts.**
Photo: Andrew Lawrence

Glulam beams under 90 mm wide are usually re-sawn from larger sizes and may therefore show glue stains and minor defects on one side. *Figure 2.32* shows making good of a loose knot with a glued-in insert for an architecturally exoposed member.

2.3.3 Laminated Veneer Lumber (LVL)

Unlike glulam, which is composed of sawn laminates, LVL is built up from thin rotary peeled veneers which are then glued together to form flat panels

(Figure 2.33). The manufacturing process is similar to plywood, except that (a) the veneers are generally aligned in one direction and (b) the short lengths of veneer in each layer are end-jointed (with a scarf joint). This enables very large and strong beams to be made – currently up to about 2 m wide x 26 m long if required. Since the veneers (typically only 3mm thick) are much thinner than the laminates in glulam, a knot in one layer will have relatively little affect on the properties of the overall section, and tests show that LVL can be up to twice as strong as sawn timber of the same species. LVL can be sold under brand names such as Kerto®, Microllam and Prolam.

2.3.4 I-Joists

I-joists, comprising an oriented strand board or open pressed metal web and solid flanges *(Figure 2.34)*, are increasingly being used for domestic floors. Though deeper and more expensive than solid timber joists of equivalent strength and stiffness, they are more stable because of the small size of the flanges. This reduces the vertical shrinkage of multi-storey platform frames and the risk of squeaking floorboards caused by differential shrinkage of the solid joists. This can lead to a gap opening between the boards and some of the joists below, or cause a few joists to lift off their supports.

Figure 2.33
Laminated Veneer Lumber (LVL) is built up from 3 mm thick peeled veneers.
Photo: Andrew Lawrence

2.3.5 Cross-laminated timber

By glueing together layers of boards in alternate directions *(Figure 2.35)*, it is possible to create very large panels of what is called cross-laminated timber. There are now several manufacturers and sheets up to about 3m x 15m x 200mm thick are commonly available, suitable for both wall and floor construction. The two-way strength of the sheets enables large openings to be cut for doors and windows without the need for lintels. For an example of the use of cross-laminated refer to *Case Study 7*: Carlisle Lane Lofts.

Figure 2.34 *(above)*
Many domestic floors are now made using I-joists.
Photo: wood for good

Figure 2.35 *(left)*
Cross-laminated timber wall and floor panels are becoming increasingly common in residential construction.

2.3.6 Board materials

These are sheet materials manufactured from wood veneers, strands, chips, or fibres. Except where noted below, they are generally derived from softwood bonded with non-moisture resistant glues under heat and pressure. Sheet sizes vary but are typically 1.2 m x 2.4 m.

While some plywoods and oriented strand boards (OSBs) are manufactured according to tight quality control procedures for structural applications, chip and fibreboards are usually only suitable for furniture, interior joinery and floor decking, since the short length and random orientation of the wood fibres means they have limited strength particularly under long-term loading (*Figure 2.05*).

Plywood

Plywoods (*Figure 2.36*) are manufactured from rotary peeled veneers, with successive veneers orientated at 90° to provide a sheet with dimensional stability and bi-directional bending strength, albeit stronger parallel to the face grain.

Figure 2.36 *(left)*
In plywood, alternate peeled veneers are turned to create a stable sheet with strength in two directions.

Figure 2.37 *(middle)*
The outer strands in Oriented Strand Board (OSB) are aligned with the principal spanning direction.

Figure 2.38 *(right)*
Chipboard is a relatively weak material because the chips are short and randomly oriented.

Structural plywoods are generally manufactured from softwood, although birch and birch faced plywoods are also available. Although they are bonded with moisture resistant glues, the timber itself is not resistant to decay and therefore not suitable for wet exposure for long periods. Unlike non-structural plywoods, structural plywoods are manufactured from structurally graded veneers, bonded under rigorous factory conditions, giving them reliable strength properties, derived from testing.

Non-structural plywoods (which may be manufactured from softwood or tropical hardwood veneers) are intended for furniture, joinery, cladding and formwork applications. These include marine plywoods (comprising moderately durable tropical hardwood veneers bonded with a moisture resistant glue); veneer plywoods (in which all the veneers are orientated with their plane parallel to the surface of the panel); decorative plywoods (with better grade face veneers sometimes coated with a phenolic film for wear and moisture resistance); and low cost blockboards (with a central core of wood strips bonded between the outer veneers).

Oriented strand board (OSB)

Oriented strand board *(Figure 2.37)* is made from large wood strands arranged in layers, alternately parallel and perpendicular to the face layer, to give strength and stiffness in two directions – similar to plywood, but of course weaker because of the shorter fibres.

Structural grades of OSB use moisture resistant glues and have reliable, albeit limited strengths, again based on testing.

Chipboard

Often called particleboard, chipboards comprise small wood chips with a resin binder *(Figure 2.38)*. The chips are formed into a mat and then compressed between heated platens. Like the fibreboards discussed below, they were originally developed to add value to forest thinnings and sawmill waste.

Fibreboard

These are reconstituted from the individual wood fibres. Although they may be bonded using adhesives, they often rely on the inherent adhesive qualities of the wood fibres.

Since the reconstituted fibres are crumpled rather than neatly aligned, fibreboards obviously have limited strength. The family of fibreboards includes the low density softboards used for thermal and sound insulation, as well as the now ubiquitous medium density fibreboard (MDF) which has a density similar to the softwood from which it was derived, and also the higher density and generally thinner hardboards.

Veneers

The production of veneers has extended the usefulness and versatility of many timbers and permits the economic use of highly decorative species which might otherwise be limited in supply. Veneers are thin slices of wood, usually glued onto panels to produce doors, tops and panels for cabinets, parquet floors, and furniture parts. These slices can either be taken from rectangular blocks of wood using a slicing machine which cuts across the growth rings, or by using a lathe which "peels" off wood from a log,

Flat or crown cutting is a common method of veneer manufacturing, which involves cutting parallel to the centre of the log. This produces a "cathedral" type grain pattern *(Figure 2.39a)*. With this method, a consistent pattern can be achieved, which means it is well suited to wall panels and furniture.

A wood-based board material with a decorative veneer often provides a more stable product than one machined from solid timber and proprietary veneered boards are widely available. The appearance and figure of veneers is markedly variable and to obtain a specific effect for prestige projects veneers can be selected personally from suppliers' stocks.

2.3.7 Modified wood

The main reason for modifying woods is to increase their durability against decay. Compared with preservative treatments, where often only the outer

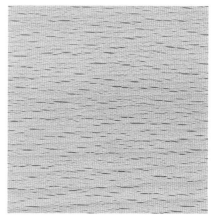

Figure 2.39
Decorative veneers.

a *(top)* **shows a crown-cut surface**; and **b** *(above)* **a rotary cut surface**. *For a quarter-cut surface see Figure 2.27*

Figure 2.40 *(right)*
Thermowood is heat-treated for increased durability, and is ideal for cladding.
Photo: Finnforest

Figure 2.41 *(above)*
Accoya is a modified pine.
Photo: BSW Timber

shell of timber is treated, one advantage of modified woods is that the full thickness of timber is modified, meaning that site cutting and drilling can be undertaken without affecting the treatment. A general introduction to two examples of modified wood is given below. Further detail is included in *Section 5.1*.

Heat-treated wood

Heat-treated wood *(Figure 2.40)* is non-durable softwood that has been heated to high temperatures to remove the 'edible' resin and some of the starches, making the timber darker, more durable and more dimensionally stable, but also weaker. It is therefore ideal for cladding but would be unsuitable for loadbearing applications. Heat treated wood is sold under brand names such as ThermoWood® and Plato® wood.

Acetylated wood

Accoya® *(Figure 2.41)* is wood which has been chemically modified by acetylation – a process in which the water within the cell walls is replaced by acetyl groups derived from acetic acid. Without water, fungi cannot survive and acetylation improves the durability and dimensional stability of timber. The combination of stability and durability makes the timber ideal for exterior joinery, but at a cost premium to less durable alternatives.

2.4 Performance in fire

The main fire performance regulations relate to the fire resistance period of the structure and the surface spread of flame. Detailed requirements are included in the Building Regulations.

2.4.1 Surface spread of flame

In larger spaces, exposed timbers may need to be painted or impregnated with a flame retardant treatment to provide Class 1 or 0 surface spread of flame resistance, in order to limit rate of spread of the fire to enable the occupants to escape. Since only the surface or outer shell of the timber is protected, treatment must be carried out after the members have been cut to final size.

Some flame retardant paints and varnishes are sensitive to moisture and may also be damaged by, for instance, over-coating during maintenance.

The kiln-drying that is required following pressure impregnation with inorganic salt flame retardants, can cause a strength loss of up to 20% and will often darken the timber. Compatibility with any glulam adhesive should be checked with the coating and adhesive manufacturer. Some salts are only suitable for interior use.

2.4.2 Period of fire resistance

Exposed timber is often limited to roofs, partly because these generally have no fire resistance requirement. In other locations, structural members are required to maintain their strength for a certain period to allow the occupants to escape.

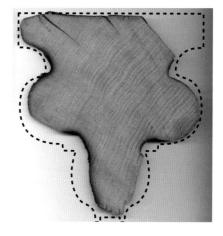

Figure 2.42
A cross section through one of the ribs salvaged from the roof of York Minster after the fire in 1984. The dotted line shows the original size of the member before charring.
Photo: Andrew Lawrence

Timber in fact has a degree of natural fire resistance. As timber burns it chars and swells *(Figure 2.42)*. Charcoal is a poor conductor and so insulates the timber behind. Combined with the high thermal insulation characteristics of timber, this ensures that the core of a timber member exposed to fire remains cool and structurally sound (compare an unprotected steel member which will quickly lose both strength and stiffness).

For softwood, the rate of charring is about 0.6 mm/minute. Therefore, to provide 30 minutes fire resistance, a member would need to be about 20 mm larger on all the exposed faces – though in practice the need for larger members is often obviated by the higher timber strengths which can be taken in the short term fire condition.

While some flame retardant varnishes will intumesce, they have no significant effect on the rate of charring and therefore the period of fire resistance.

Metal fixings also need to be protected, usually with a timber cap. Clearly over-sizing members in this way would be uneconomic for thin domestic joists and wall studs, and so they are instead protected behind a layer of plasterboard.

2.5 Surface finishes

This section concentrates on applied finishes. Sawing and planing are briefly discussed in *Section 4.2*. Glulam appearance grades are discussed in *Section 2.3.2*.

Applied finishes for exterior timber

Without protection, all fully exposed external timber will eventually weather to a grey *(Figure 2.15)* due to the action of UV light. Exterior finishes can be used to prevent such bleaching and particularly the uneven weathering that might result from, for instance, the partial protection offered by an overhanging roof, as well as to limit the surface checking and splitting that result from alternate cycles of wetting and drying.

Paints and varnishes

Paints are opaque and should offer a life of several years, although they are relatively labour-intensive to maintain. On resinous timbers such as pine and Douglas fir there is a risk of unsightly resin exuding from the knots, particularly where dark coatings are used on southern aspects leading to higher heat gains.

Varnishes are very similar to paints but without pigments. Because they are colourless, they rapidly embrittle under ultra-violet radiation, causing premature flaking of the varnish *(Figure 2.43)* and surface degradation of the timber below. They are therefore not recommended for exterior use, unless the client is prepared to accept a very expensive annual maintenance regime.

Figure 2.43
Varnishes quickly break down under ultraviolet light and are not recommended for external exposure.
Photo: TRADA Technology

Woodstains

Woodstains can be gloss or matt, and vary from almost colourless to almost opaque. They are lower build than paints and varnishes leaving a much thinner film on the surface of the timber *(Figure 2.44)*. They therefore allow the timber to breathe, while acting as a water repellent.

Their main advantage is ease of maintenance, which usually consists of washing down to remove the products of surface weathering and any loose particles, followed by re-application. More opaque stains require less maintenance because they screen the surface of the timber from harmful ultraviolet radiation. However, darker stains require more maintenance because the higher thermal gains lead to larger moisture movements of the timber, which can then damage the finish.

Some hardwoods can be difficult to coat with low-build stains, because their density and the presence of extractives inhibit penetration of the stain.

Figure 2.44
Woodstains leave only a very thin film on the surface of the timber.

End-grain sealants

Water is absorbed into the end grain of timber much faster than it is across the grain (from several times to several thousand times, depending on species). Such water penetration can lead to splitting, distortion, failure of surface coatings, staining, mould or decay and delamination of veneers in panel products. For this reason it is important to protect the end grain by an end grain sealant that prevents or retards the absorption of water under damp or wet conditions.

Primers and stains offer adequate protection for the end grain of solid timber used in joinery. The edges of wood-based boards can be sealed with:

- Liquid sealants suitable for brush, roller or spray applications.

- Paste sealants applied by trowelling. Suitable for the treatment of individual boards in small quantities.

- Solids applied in melted form by various methods

- Self adhesive tapes produced in wide variety of forms for different end uses.

Good design should be the first means of reducing moisture penetration through the end grains of timber and panel products with sealants being used as a supplement.

Other issues

The appearance of external timbers can be affected by exudation of tannins and resins. Tannin is mainly an issue with oak, which will slowly exude over the first year or so (even from kiln dried material) and can stain adjacent surfaces; it also corrodes mild steel. Species which are known to exude resin in hot weather include Douglas fir, larch and European redwood.

Applied finishes for interior timber

This subject is generally beyond the scope of this book. For internal members which are to be left unfinished it is wise to apply a clear primer in the factory, for protection against dirt and water staining during construction.

2.6 Preservatives

Preservatives are used to improve the durability of non-durable timbers, primarily the softwoods, by preventing the growth of timber-destroying fungi, as well as surface mould growth and insect attack.

Preservatives can be poisonous, not only to fungi, but sometimes also to mankind and wildlife. They are therefore becoming increasingly restricted on health and environmental grounds, encouraging a gradual move towards the use of naturally durable timbers, where there is a risk of decay.

So called brush-applied preservatives barely penetrate the timber. They need to be regularly re-applied and even then are of limited value except in stopping surface mould growth.

There are three requirements for effective preservative treatment:

- The preservative needs to be applied under pressure in a vacuum tank so that it penetrates deep into the timber.

- The timber needs to be sufficiently dry to aid penetration.

- A sufficiently permeable species needs to be used (typically Scots pine).

If the above requirements are met, more or less complete penetration of the sapwood can be achieved, if the treatment time is long enough. While the heartwood is less permeable it does, depending on species, have a degree of inherent natural durability. If treating a finished glulam, some sapwood in the centre of the member will also remain untreated since both the glue lines and the heartwood block penetration of the preservative. It is interesting to note that through-thickness treatment of LVL and plywood can be achieved thanks to the micro-fissures generated by flattening of the peeled veneers.

There are currently three types of preservative in general use – oil-borne, waterborne, and organic solvent-borne.

The oil-borne preservatives (traditionally creosote) tend to be the most effective. This is because the oil acts as a moisture barrier, keeping the timber drier and reducing the risk of fissuring due to rapid surface drying which might allow water to reach the untreated heartwood. The use of such preservatives in fully external structures over many years certainly suggests they can achieve at least a 50 year design life. Obviously the oily surface of the timber cannot be glued, so that treatment must be carried out after fabrication of glulam members and ideally after all cutting and drilling to ensure that the timber exposed at the surface is fully treated. The disadvantages of oil-borne treatments are that the oil is not chemically fixed to the timber and can therefore stain clothes or leach out (particularly in hot weather); they also carry a noticeable odour. There are also potential health and environmental risks, although given the tiny amount of oil that does leach out, the latter are probably more perceived than actual. In the UK, creosote is now only permitted for telegraph poles and railway sleepers.

The main alternative to oil-borne treatments, particularly for members in human contact (such as handrails and decking), is to use waterborne preservatives. These generally include copper which imparts a green colour to the timber (Figure 2.45). The traditional waterborne preservative was CCA (copper chrome arsenic) but following restrictions on the use of both chrome and arsenic, this has now been superseded by the modern copper organic fungicides. In theory CCA may still be used in limited applications but in practice the market is so small that it is no longer economic for treatment plants to offer it. Although the waterborne preservatives are still toxic (it is of course this toxicity which prevents the fungal growth), they have the advantage of being chemically fixed to the timber.

Figure 2.45
Waterborne preservatives generally incorporate copper, which imparts a green colour to the timber.

For glulam, it is most common to treat the completed member – chiefly because the treated laminates are relatively difficult to glue. However, post-treatment drying shrinkage of a large glulam member after the wet treatment process will tend to generate fissures exposing the untreated heartwood as well as the untreated sapwood in the middle of the member. The alternative is to treat the laminates before glueing (thereby achieving full sapwood penetration of permeable species such as European redwood), although without the moisture barrier provided by the oil-borne treatments, there still remains the risk of subsequent fissuring of the completed glulam in hot weather, exposing the untreated timber. While there is little long term field data available on the efficacy of the modern waterborne formulations, the combination of the fissuring (discussed above), reduced chemical fixation and reduced toxicity levels of the modern CCA replacements suggests that they are likely to offer a shorter life than the traditional oil-borne treatments. For example, in the UK the BWPDA currently indicates only a 30-year design life for members exposed to wetting. A final disadvantage of the waterborne treatments is that the wet treatment process causes swelling and distortion of the timber as well as raised grain, making them unsuitable for joinery applications.

The best preservatives for joinery are those based on organic fungicides and insecticides, carried in an organic solvent. Being borne by light organic solvents (for instance white spirit) rather than water, they do not cause wetting distortion of the timber. They do, however, need a protective coat of paint to prevent leaching. They are also under pressure from legislation to limit solvent emissions and are slowly being replaced by micro-emulsions. These micro-emulsions rely on the same active ingredients, but now dissolved in a small quantity of strong solvent, which is then mixed with emulsifiers, allowing subsequent dilution with about twenty times the volume of water. Although some swelling of the joinery occurs, this is much less than with the waterborne preservatives discussed above.

Table 2.1 Properties and uses of common species

Species [1]	Main origin	Strength & density	Durability [2]	Moisture movement	Cost [3]	Structure	Interior joinery	Cladding	Decking	Case Studies
Softwoods										
European spruce	Europe Russia	Medium	Slightly durable	Medium	Low	✓	✓			11
European redwood [4] (*Scots pine*)	Europe Russia	Medium	Slightly to Moderately durable	Medium	Low	✓	✓	✓ Preservative treated	✓ Preservative treated	
European larch	Europe Russia	Medium	Slightly to Moderately durable	Small	Medium	✓		✓	✓	10, 13,14,15
Douglas fir [4]	North America	Medium	Moderately durable	Small	Medium	✓		✓	✓	6,14,16
Western red cedar	North America	Low	Durable	Small	High			✓		11
Temperate Hardwoods										
European oak [5]	Western Europe	High	Durable	Medium	High [6]	✓	✓	✓	✓	9, 10, 11, 16, 18, 21, 22
Beech	Western Europe	High	Not durable	Large	High		✓			—
European birch	Europe	High	Not durable	Large	High		✓			10, 13, 19, 20
Sweet chestnut	Western Europe	Medium	Durable	Small	High		✓	✓		—
Tulipwood	USA	Medium	Slightly durable	Medium	High	✓	✓		✓	—
American black walnut	USA	High	Moderately durable	Medium	High		✓			—
American white oak	USA	High	Moderately Durable to Durable	Medium	High	✓	✓			6, 8, 12
Hard maple	USA	USA	Slightly durable	Medium	High					—

Species [1]	Main origin	Strength & density	Durability [2]	Moisture movement	Cost [3]	Common uses				Case Studies
						Structure	Interior joinery	Cladding	Decking	
Tropical Hardwoods										
Angelim	Brazil	High	(Durable)	Small	High	✓	✓	✓	✓	—
Cumaru	Brazil	Very high	(Very durable)	Medium	High	✓		✓	✓	—
Ekki	W Africa	Very high	Durable	Large	High	✓				—
Greenheart	Guyana	Very high	Very durable	Medium	High	✓				—
Iroko	Guyana	High	Durable to very durable	Small	High	✓	✓	✓	✓	—
Jatoba	Brazil	Very high	(Durable)	Medium	High	✓	✓	✓		—
Massaran-duba	Brazil	Very high	(Very durable)		High	✓		✓	✓	—
Red louro	Brazil	High	Durable		High		✓	✓	✓	—
Tatajuba	Brazil	High	(Durable)	Medium	High	✓	✓	✓	✓	—

Notes

1   Refer to suppliers for a full list of available hardwood species and the availability of certified timber. Threatened species are listed on the IUCN Red List and CITES (the Convention on International Trade in Endangered Species) seeks to limit trade in the more endangered species (which are listed in the CITES appendices).

2   Durability of heartwood against fungal attack from BS EN 350. Note that sapwood of all species is non-durable. Bracketed classifications are approximate, indicating that species are not included in BS EN 350, generally because there is no long term test data. Fast grown UK softwood is generally less durable.

3   Note that in practice fabrication and assembly costs often dominate.

4   Risk of resin exudation on hot days.

5   Exudes tannin on first year or so when used externally.

6   Indicates cost of kiln dried timber. Green oak is considerably cheaper.

3

Connections

Peter Ross

As a building material, timber is relatively lightweight and easily worked. In consequence, there are many ways of connecting timber members, both to each other and to other components of the building frame. These methods can be grouped under three broad headings – all-timber connections; metal connections; and adhesives.

**Marlow Academy node
connection detail.**

As a building material, timber is relatively lightweight and easily worked. In consequence, there are many ways of connecting timber members, both to each other and to other components of the building frame. These methods can be grouped under three broad headings – *all-timber connections; metal connections; and adhesives.*

As noted in *Section 2.1.1* timber is a markedly directional material, and the strength of a connection is usually determined by the timber properties in the weaker direction (ie perpendicular to the grain) in either compression, shear, or tension.

Figure 3.01 illustrates some common connection arrangements. In traditional framing, the capacity of a post at its base *(Figure 3.01a)* is actually determined by the strength of the bottom rail in compression perpendicular to the grain, which is roughly one quarter of the parallel-to-the-grain value. Similarly, the capacity of a wedged tenon *(Figure 3.01b)* could be limited by the shear strength of the section beyond the mortice, which in turn is roughly half of

**Figure 3.01
Common connection arrangements.**

a *(top left)*
A post bearing on a bottom rail

b *(top right)*
A traditional wedged tenon

c *(bottom left)*
Early failure of a bolted joint due to sub-standard edge distances A, spacing B, and loaded end distance C, causing splitting along Y

d *(bottom right)*
To maximise joint strength, edge distances A should be about 3d (where d is the bolt diameter); spacing B around 4d; and loaded end distances C about 7d. Washer diameters should be at least 3d

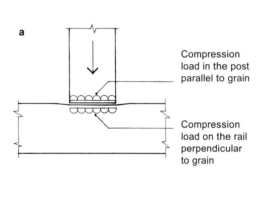

a

Compression load in the post parallel to grain

Compression load on the rail perpendicular to grain

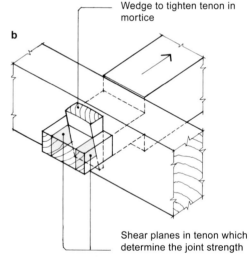

b

Wedge to tighten tenon in mortice

Shear planes in tenon which determine the joint strength

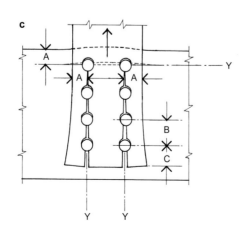

c

Y

A
A   A

B

C

Y   Y

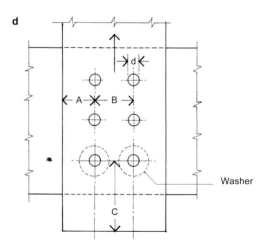

d

d

A   B

C

Washer

the perpendicular-to-the-grain value. The proportions of traditional framing joints take account of these material properties, since they developed on Darwinian principles, and they are used with confidence by framers.

Metal fasteners under load also produce a splitting action in the timber (*Figure 3.01c*), which is effectively a tension perpendicular to the grain. In order to avoid this form of failure, the design code gives rules for minimum fastener spacings, as well as edge and end distances (*Figure 3.01d*). Bolt groups in timber will thus appear to be generously spaced compared to groups in steel members, and will have larger washers – again because of the limits imposed by compression perpendicular to the grain.

The above considerations mean that connections should not be left to the end of the design process. Indeed, for trusses and frames it is essential for an outline joint solution to lead the design of the members themselves.

Figures 3.02
The Guildhall,
Lavenham, Suffolk.

3.1 All-timber connections

Connections made entirely of timber have been in use for many centuries. They are the basis of the medieval frames which can still be seen in ancient towns and cities *(Figure 3.02)*, and are still a valid form of connection for the frames shown in *Section 4.2*.

The species of timber used in these structures was generally oak or chestnut; and, except for small components such as pegs, the material was used 'green' – that is to say unseasoned. The use of green timber may be surprising, since most present-day specifications call for 'dry' timber, but in the context of traditional, or heavy framing, green timber has several advantages:

- Drying time
  Oak dries very slowly. Typical frame members – say 150 mm to 200 mm square – will take some six to eight years' air-drying to lose all their surplus moisture, and kilning does not greatly shorten the drying period for timber of these thicknesses. Since oak frames have always been individually designed there are no stocks of material, and the project would effectively be on hold for this period.

- Hardness
  Even using power tools, seasoned oak is much more difficult to cut and shape than material in the green state. Anyone who has pruned roses will appreciate the difference between a live shoot and a dead branch.

- Drying movement
  Oak has a large coefficient of drying shrinkage across the grain. Seasoned members would all require a second cut after drying in order to true up the faces, otherwise the joints could not fit accurately.

- Fissures
  Seasoned oak has a marked tendency to fissure. Fissures complicate the cutting of joints, and make edge moulding particularly difficult.

The consequence of all this is that a frame in seasoned oak, whether medieval or modern, is simply not a commercial proposition. Green oak gives advantages of conversion and working, although it must be borne in mind that the drying movements which might have dissipated while the timber was stacked in the yard will now occur in service. It is an obvious requirement that the frame should nevertheless remain stable, with no slackness developing in the assembly. The vocabulary of traditional joints was developed over time to maintain the joint tightness through this drying process. Working with green oak is described in more detail in the TRADA publication, *Green oak in construction*.

A small selection of traditional framing joints are illustrated in *Figure 3.03a* In general they rely on mechanical interlock as the principal method of load transmission and use pegs, made of seasoned oak, as a tightening and locking mechanism. The joints most often used by carpenters today include:

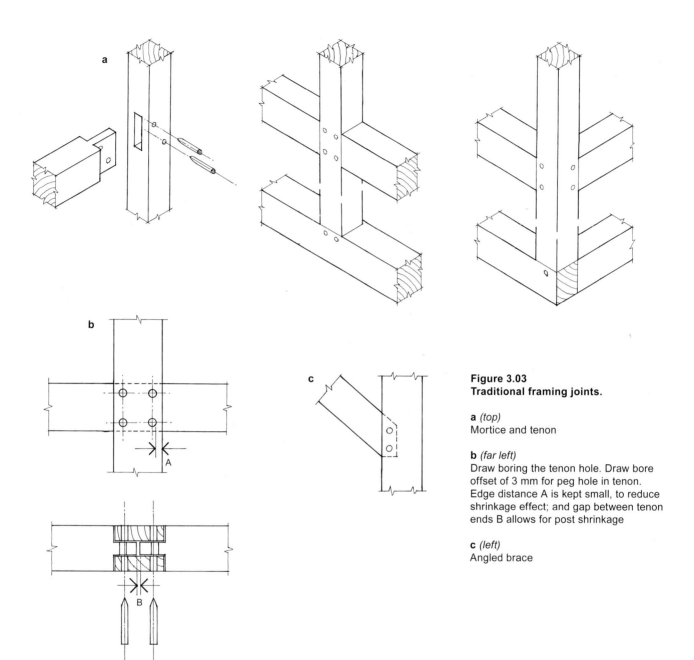

Figure 3.03
Traditional framing joints.

a *(top)*
Mortice and tenon

b *(far left)*
Draw boring the tenon hole. Draw bore offset of 3 mm for peg hole in tenon. Edge distance A is kept small, to reduce shrinkage effect; and gap between tenon ends B allows for post shrinkage

c *(left)*
Angled brace

- The mortice and tenon

  This is the basic joint for all framing work (*Figure 3.03a*). Compression loads are passed on through bearing on the tenon shoulders, and shear loads through side-bearing of the tenon within the mortice. The pegs, which are slightly tapered, are set in holes close to the bearing edge and the holes themselves are 'draw bored', whereby the hole in the tenon is offset by about 3 mm from the holes in the mortice housing (*Figure 3.03b*). The action of driving the pegs home draws the two members into tight contact, and the residual deformation of the peg absorbs any drying shrinkage effect. The joint for an angled brace (*Figure 3.03c*) is a simple variation of the right-angled joint.

- Lap joints
 The notched lap *(Figure 3.04a)* achieves a small degree of tensile strength through the shear capacity of the notch. End laps, which provide more tensile resistance, include the wedged dovetail tenon *(Figure 3.04b)* and the wedged tenon *(Figure 3.01b)*. The wedge in the latter joint has considerable lightening power (given sufficient end distance on the tenon), and can mobilise significant bending as well as tension resistance. Both wedges can be re-driven to take up drying shrinkage.

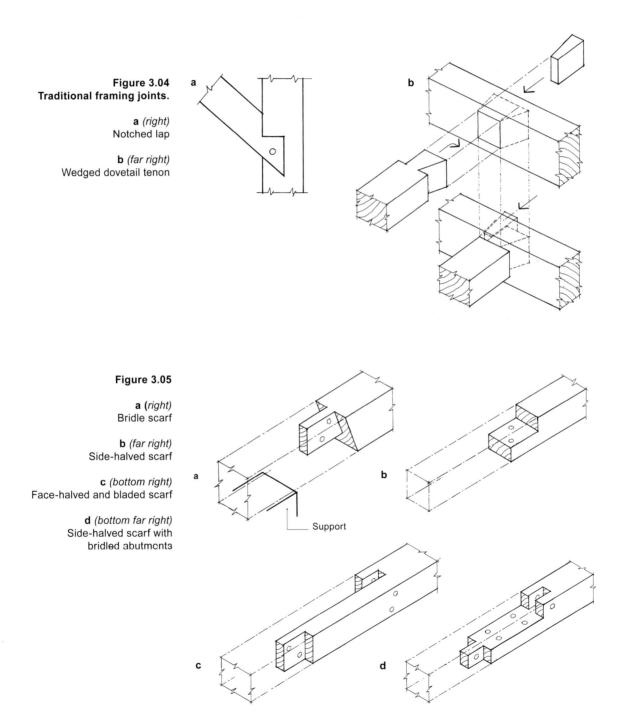

Figure 3.04
Traditional framing joints.

a *(right)*
Notched lap

b *(far right)*
Wedged dovetail tenon

Figure 3.05

a (right*)*
Bridle scarf

b *(far right)*
Side-halved scarf

c *(bottom right)*
Face-halved and bladed scarf

d *(bottom far right)*
Side-halved scarf with
bridled abutments

Support

- Scarf joints

  A scarf joint connects individual pieces to provide a member which is longer than can be provided in a single piece. Common examples are wall plates and purlins. Where possible the scarf is placed at points of low bending stress – for instance, in a wall plate, close to the supports. There the load is principally in shear, which can be resisted by the bridle scarf *(Figure 3.05a)* or a simple side-halved scarf *(Figure 3.05b)*. Providing a scarf joint which has a degree of bending resistance requires a longer overlap between the members. Those in common use today are the face-halved and bladed scarf *(Figure 3.05c)* and the side-halved scarf with bridled abutments *(Figure 3.05d)*. The latter joint is stiffer, since it retains the full depth of the pieces throughout, but for strength, both of these joints rely on the pegs, which will only give some 15% to 25% of the strength of the equivalent unjointed section.

- The tie beam lap dovetail

  This particularly complex joint occurs in traditional framing where a post supports a roof truss, while being laterally stabilised by the wall plate. To allow all this to happen, the post is locally widened (referred to as the jowl) *(Figure 3.06)*.

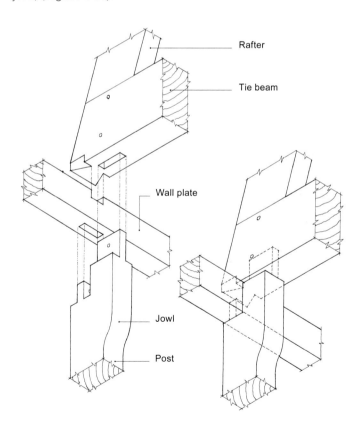

Rafter

Tie beam

Wall plate

Jowl

Post

Figure 3.06
Tie beam lapped dovetail.

These joints were developed for green material, using only timber. Within the vocabulary of traditional construction, their rationale is evident, and so they are visually satisfying. Nevertheless, they require specialist skills, are relatively labour-intensive, and have limited capacity in tension and bending. For frames of seasoned timber, the use of metal will improve capacity, and in general will be more economic.

3.2 Metal connections

From the seventeenth century onward, the all-timber frame gradually gave way to a standard construction of masonry walls with only the intermediate floors and roof trusses in timber. Larger spans and shallower pitches, the latter enabled by the use of slate covering, produced higher loads in the truss rafters, resulting in a gradual introduction of metal strapwork to reinforce their connections to the bottom tie *(Figure 3.07)*.

From the inventiveness of the industrial revolution emerged the first patents for the mass production of **nails**, **screws** and **bolts**. This resulted in a dramatic reduction of their costs, which led in turn to a fundamental change in truss construction. Throughout history, truss members had been set in a single plane, with their ends shaped to fit one another. If, instead, they were lapped, members could simply be nailed or bolted together. As reliance could now be placed on the fasteners acting in shear, the joint itself would now be equally strong in compression and tension, the latter being the weakness of the traditional joint. The principle can be extended to join three or more layers of timber together *(Figure 3.08a)*. However, it will be seen that the fasteners are limited to the overlap areas of the timber, and this may in turn limit the overall joint capacity.

Figure 3.07 *(right)*
Metal strapwork to traditional trusses

a
Ridge detail

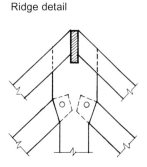

b
Rafter to bottom tie connection

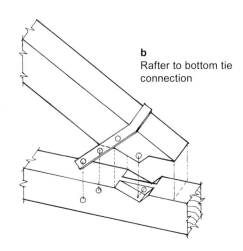

c
Centre tie to kingpost: threaded bolt

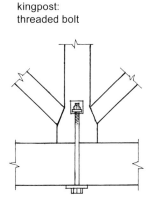

d
Centre tie to kingpost: strap with folding wedges

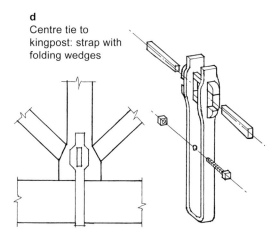

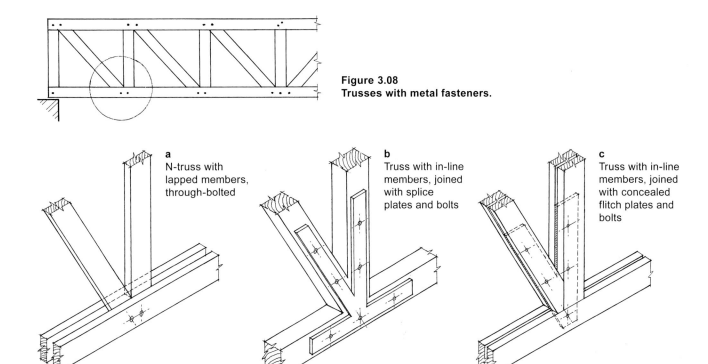

**Figure 3.08
Trusses with metal fasteners.**

a
N-truss with lapped members, through-bolted

b
Truss with in-line members, joined with splice plates and bolts

c
Truss with in-line members, joined with concealed flitch plates and bolts

As a further development of this idea, profiled steel flats can be fabricated, matching the member profiles, either as splice plates *(Figure 3.08b)* or flitch plates *(Figure 3.08c)*. In these cases, the timber members return to a common plane, and a flitch plate may be virtually concealed within the timber profile.

An additional advantage of this system is that the steel 'arms' along each timber member may be as long as is necessary to accommodate the required number of fasteners, and so these joints do not impose a limit on the assembly capacity. They are effectively fabricated steel components, which connect together the separate timber members. Many contemporary structures use this form, clearly expressing the separate functions of the connecting node (in steel) and the frame members (in timber). Four examples, all different in their detailing, are shown in *(Figure 3.09)*.

Purpose-made steel components are also a useful way of distributing a stress over a timber section at a point of load concentration, such as the base of a three-pinned arch *(Figure 3.10)*. Here, an inverted steel T-section has been let into the base of the glulam, and bolts inserted through the web, with the heads recessed and plugged. A similar detail is used at the crown.

A post-war development, which achieved almost overnight success, was the **pressed metal plate fastener** (often referred to as a 'gangnail' from the first proprietary product). As the names suggest, the 'nails' are first pressed out of a plate. Two plates are applied to a joint as splices, and pressed home. The plates are used principally in the fabrication of roof trusses, which are assembled on a flat bed equipped with a travelling hydraulic press *(Figures 3.11a-d)*.

Figure 3.09
Joints with metal nodes.

a *(bottom far left)*
Alnwick Castle Visitor Centre *(see Case Study 15)*. Perimeter posts support splayed struts and a dia-grid roof, all in larch

b *(top far left)*
Alnwick roof node connection detail. A short section of square hollow section tube, with a flitch blade welded to each corner, all painted. A downward extension of the blade picks up steel tension rods

c *(bottom left)*
Portcullis House courtyard roof, Westminster *(see Case Study 12)*. Corner 'cigar' columns supporting a barrel vault.

d *(left)*
Portcullis roof node connection detail. A spherical node, with welded flitch plates, all in stainless steel. The joint transmits both compressive forces (by bolts) and bending moments (by top and bottom bearing plates).

Figure 3.09 *(continued)*

e *(left)*
Haberdashers' Hall foyer roof during construction *(see Case Study 8)*, showing the principal rafters in glulam, infilled with purlins which support the roof over and the ceiling below.

f *(middle)*
Haberdashers' Hall eaves node detail. The end shoe of the glulams bears on a triangular base-plate, which also connects to the stabilising tie-rods. All in stainless steel, reminiscent of yacht rigging.

g *(right)*
Marlow Academy node connection detail. The curved Kerto members bear directly on the node, which is a short length of stainless steel circular hollow section. The connections are made with Cowley Connectors into threaded holes. An access slot for the screwdriver is seen on the left.

h *(below)*
Roof of Marlow Academy, Ramsgate – see also *Figure 4.21*. Kerto deck cut to taper, with loose tongue edge joints.
Architect: *BDP;*
Engineers: *BDP and Capita Symonds;*
Timber engineer: *Cowley Timberwork.*

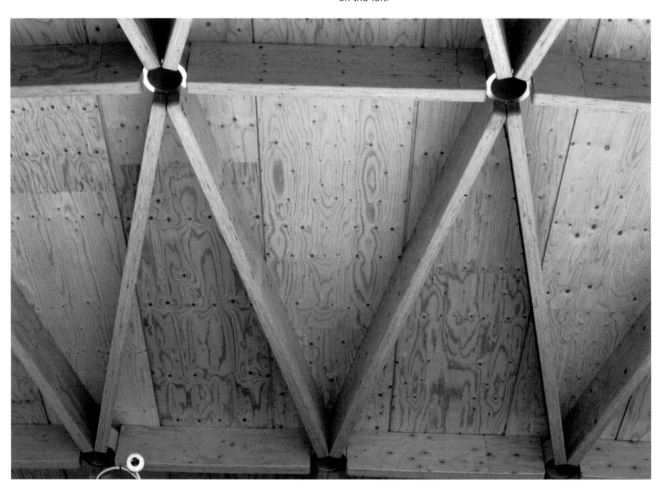

Production rates for components using small fasteners speeded up with the introduction of gun-nails, and machine-driven screws, which, with thinner shanks, avoided the need for pre-drilling. In joints such as *(Figure 3.08c)* dowels could be substituted for bolts, and would be visually much less evident. Dowels are normally inserted into tight-fitting holes to hold the members together, which also reduces the tendency of the joint to slip under load. For a large fastener group, this would require extreme accuracy in the drilling of the components, leading to the development of 'self-drilling' dowels, capable of cutting through timber and up to 15 mm of steel, in two or perhaps three layers. Thus an in-line connection can be made between two members, as shown in *(Figure 3.12)*, with blank flitch plates installed in end slots and the dowels installed by drilling. The dowel diameters lie between 5 mm and 7 mm, with a maximum length of 220 mm. Using multiple plates maximises the joint capacity.

Other metal fixings include split rings and shear plate connectors, but these are labour-intensive specialist fittings and fall outside the general commercial range.

3.3 Adhesives

The invention in the 1930s of adhesives which were water-resistant was a great leap forward, enabling the fabrication of structural glulam elements which are far larger than can be cut from solid timber. The manufacturing process is described in *Section 2.3.2.*

Figure 3.10
Littledown Sports Centre *(see Figure 4.13)* **arch base. To collect the compression load of the arch and pass it into the base pin, an inverted steel T-section has been let into the base of the glulam, with the bolt heads recessed and plugged.**
Architect: Saunders Architects

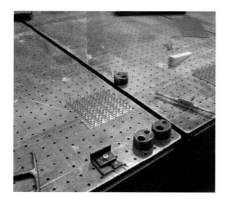

Figure 3.11a-d
Trussed rafter manufacture.

a *(top left)*
The truss is set out on the assembly table, with locating guides, and the lower plates positioned.

b *(top right)*
Precut timber is laid in position, located by the guides.

c *(bottom left)*
The top plates are positioned.

d *(bottom right)*
A hydraulic press moves along the table, pressing the plates home.

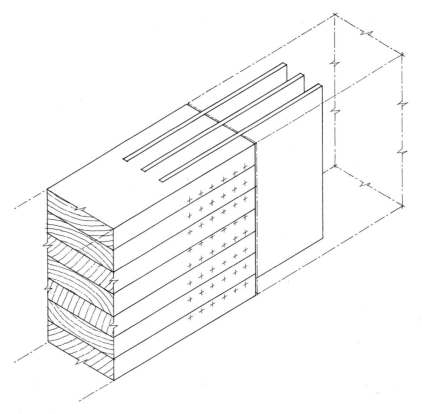

Figure 3.12
In-line connection between
two glulam beams. Three
blank flitch-plates are set in
pre-cut slots, and then fixed
by self-drilling dowels.

3.3.1 Formaldehyde adhesives

These adhesives are very efficient when used in glue lines parallel to the grain, and if correctly applied, are stronger than the timber itself. Routine splitting tests on plywood samples, for instance, would be expected to show that the majority of the fracture had taken place in the adjacent timber. The glue cannot effectively 'get a grip' on end grain, and so individual laminates are end-connected with finger joints – effectively a long scarf joint folded back on itself to minimise waste.

A glued joint is completely rigid, with a brittle failure mode. It cannot therefore be used in a strength combination with bolts, since the glue would take all the load, fail, and pass the load to the bolts, which need a small embedment movement to take up load.

Since the formaldehyde adhesives are also thermosetting, thick joints have to be avoided, to prevent excessive heat build-up reducing the final strength. And while they have a very high adhesion to timber, they do not adhere to metal. In the 1960s a new product range, based on resins, extended the application of adhesives to timber construction.

3.3.2 Resin adhesives

The range of proprietary resin adhesives will bond to most materials, including steel, and are more tolerant of thicker beds. They are used, among other applications, for bonding threaded rods into holes drilled into the timber *(Figure 3.13)*. This is potentially a useful way of assembling a frame, but the projecting threads are vulnerable during the assembly process, and obviously cannot be screwed into a socket, since they cannot be rotated. They must penetrate the member, to receive restraining nuts.

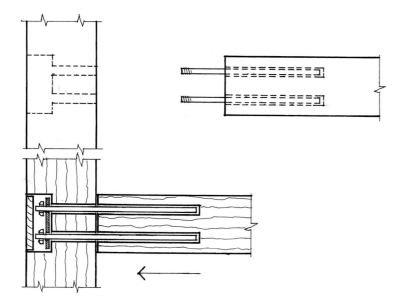

Figure 3.13
Resin-anchored bolts used to form a moment-resisting beam to post joint. The joint can be completely concealed by an infill timber, which also gives the joint a degree of fire resistance.

The *Cowley Connector*, which is a patented system, overcomes these problems and has the additional attraction of being completely contained within the timber profile. The connector *(Figure 3.14)* comprises a steel tube epoxied into the member end, which contains a threaded bolt. The head of the bolt (inside the timber) is reached through an inclined hole, emerging through the member side, down which a specially-formed spanner can reach the bolt head and tighten it in a female socket epoxied into the connected timber.

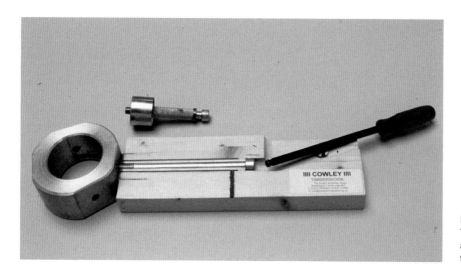

Figure 3.14
The Cowley Connector. This is a cut-away section, illustrating the joint in Figure 3.09g.

3.3.3 Polyurethane adhesives

All the adhesives discussed so far require dry timber. The most recently developed adhesives, in the polyurethane range, are moisture-tolerant and have a particular application in gridshell roof construction – see *Section 4.1.5*.

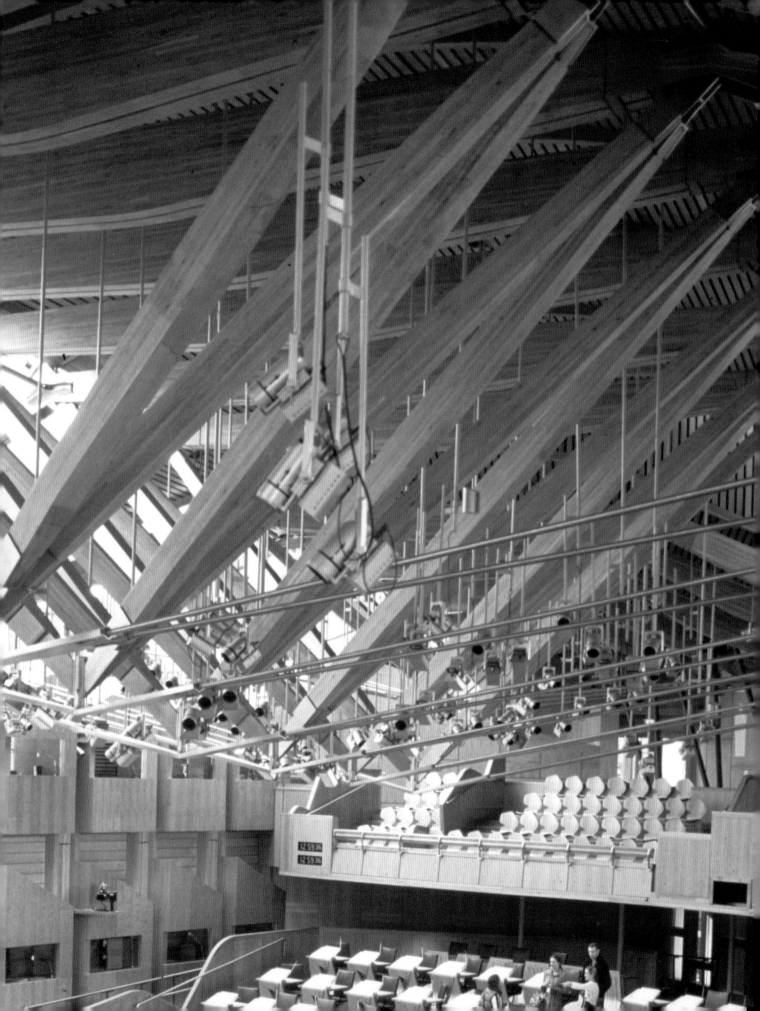

4 Applications

Peter Ross

This chapter gives guidance on the great variety of structural forms that can now be achieved in timber, and the ways in which the main generic forms can be applied to span space, as roofs, or to create whole building frames. It also deals with secondary elements within these structures (timber windows, doors, and louvres) and with timber cladding to weatherproof the structure.

The Scottish National
Parliament in Edinburgh.

In addition to the traditional construction forms, the development of durable adhesives *(see Sections 2.3.2, 2.3.3 and 3.3)* and a range of metal fasteners *(see Section 3.2)* has further enlarged the range of wood-based materials and connections which are now available to the present-day designer. Their applications, in terms of generic structural forms, are described here in their basic groupings. The sequence starts with **roofs** and **frames**, which are normally contained within the weather envelope of the building; followed by **external joinery**, which is generally exposed to the weather on one face; and finally **external structures**, where durability is often the principal design issue.

4.1 Roofs

Figure 4.01
The Burrell Museum, Glasgow.
Architect: *Barry Gasson Architects*

a *(right)*
Duo-pitch glazing, supported by glulam rafters and purlins. Restraining metal ties to the feet of the principal rafters.

b *(above)*
Flat roof, with boards on rafters and purlins.

Timber is particularly suitable for the construction of roofs, because:

- It has a high strength-to-weight ratio (being the material of choice for early flying machines).

- The structure is generally protected, and will remain dry. Thus the durability of the species is not an issue.

- There is not usually a requirement for a period of fire resistance, which would impose minimum sizes on members, and require some form of protection to metal components.

For these reasons, the roof is the predominant area of application of timber, and to take advantage of the material's visual appeal, many are designed as 'open' (ie exposed) structures, even though this requires a more detailed consideration of the connection design and service locations.

4.1.1 Beams and trusses
At its simplest, a roof structure can be made with a system of purlins and rafters. Solid timber will suffice for smaller spans, but roofs much beyond a domestic scale will require glulam or other engineered wood product members *(Figure 4.01a) (see also Section 2.3)*.

For a pitched roof with open space below, however, a truss with rafters and purlins over is generally a more efficient and a visually more interesting solution. There are a great variety of forms ranging from **traditional** construction, made almost entirely of timber, to **lapped** construction using metal connectors such as bolts or dowels, and **composite** construction, where some timber members are replaced with metal components. Taking these in turn:

- Traditional construction
  Hundreds of medieval churches and barns provide a country-wide pattern book of roof forms, of great variety. Many are original, in 'green' oak with all-timber connections *(see Section 3.1)*, but inevitably some are replacements *(Figure 4.03)*. Post-medieval roofs were based largely

Figure 4.02
Roof of the Maggie Centre, Dundee.
Architect: Frank Gehry Architects;
Engineer: Arup

a *(top)*
Exterior.

b *(above)*
Curved purlins cut from Kerto, with a Kerto deck.

Figure 4.03 *(left)*
The roof of Pilton Barn rebuilt in accordance with the original design after historical research.
Framer: McCurdy and Co

on the kingpost *(Figure 4.04a)* and queenpost *(Figure 4.04b)* trusses, appropriate for spans of between 5 m and 20 m. For larger spans in solid timber, the bottom tie may have to be made of two pieces with a tension connection. The queenpost truss has the advantages of reducing the lengths of timber needed to make the rafters and a central bay free of triangulation (although this makes it more vulnerable to asymmetric loading). While these trusses were originally concealed above a ceiling, they are handsome forms and can be exposed with advantage. If the horizontal tie is found to be too obtrusive, the earlier arch-braced *(Figure 4.04c)* or scissor trusses *(Figure 4.04d)* are alternative solutions, although they may produce an outward thrust at the base which would have to be taken into account in the design of the supports, as noted in *Section 4.1.2* below.

Figure 4.04
Truss types.

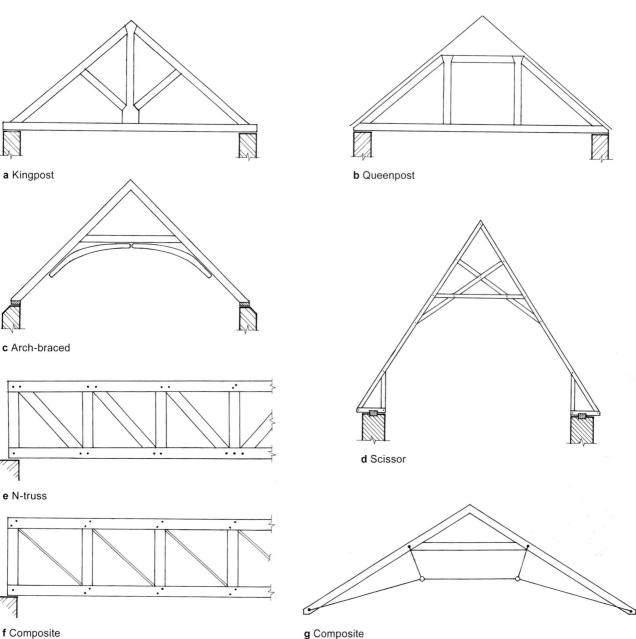

a Kingpost

b Queenpost

c Arch-braced

d Scissor

e N-truss

f Composite

g Composite

- Lapped construction
  This was introduced in the later part of the nineteenth century, and using the joints described in *Section 3.2* it opened up new forms for truss assembly. The Belfast truss *(Figure 4.05)* consists entirely of lapped members nailed together, achieving spans of up to 30 m from individual pieces no more than 7 m long. Forms such as the N-truss *(Figure 4.04e)* et seq, which relies partly on joints in tension, could now be made in timber using two- or three-element members with the bolts in multiple shear *(Figure 3.08)*.

- Composite construction
  These forms, in which timber members in tension are replaced by slender metal components, were a natural development for large-span trusses *(Figure 4.04f,g)*. The reduction in cross-section can lighten the appearance of the truss as a whole, and provide the visual satisfaction of seeing the logic of the internal truss forces expressed in the choice of material *(Figures 4.06, 4.07)*. Threading the ends of tension rods allows a simple form of connection – a restraining nut – which at the same time can be adjusted slightly to take up assembly tolerances. Steel connections may become points of interest in their own right, elaborating the forms beyond the strict demands of the engineering requirements as seen in *Figures 4.08* and *4.09*.

Figure 4.05 *(left)*
World War 1 hangars at Duxford, Cambridge. All timbers lapped and nailed.

Figure 4.06 *(above)*
The Maltings concert hall at Snape. A composite roof – steel rods in tension; timber in compression.
Architect/engineer: *Arup Associates*

Figure 4.07
Bedlington Golf Clubhouse (in course of construction).
Architect: Faulkner-Brown, Hendy; Watkinson Stonor;
Engineer: Arup

a *(top left)*
Ridge truss, consisting of lapped timbers with rod tension members.

b *(middle left)*
Connection detail. Rod diagonal penetrates the vertical, with restraining nut and washer.

Figure 4.08 *(top right)*
The Scottish National Parliament in Edinburgh. A complex roof, triangulated in both directions.
Architect: Enric Miralles/RMJM;
Engineer: Arup

Figure 4.09 *(right)*
The Scottish National Parliament. Truss node as artwork – a typical connection detail.

4.1.2 Arches

The arch *(Figure 4.10)* is regarded as the most efficient form for spanning space. It is efficient because it carries its load in compression using the whole of the cross-section, whereas beams, which act in bending, use predominantly the outer fibres. However, in preparing an arch design, the following points should be remembered:

- The arch exerts an out-thrust on its supports, and a means must be found for resisting this.

- The triangular spaces formed at the base *(Figure 4.10a)* are sometimes difficult to deal with architecturally.

- Efficiency is reduced for non-uniform loads (such as wind pressure or snow) which are carried in bending *(Figure 4.10b)*. As the arch is an element in compression, it is also prone to buckling, both in- and out-of-plane.

To deal with the out-thrust, arches are sometimes founded at ground level, using the building base slab as a 'free' support (although it has to be suitably reinforced). This geometry creates the awkward space where the arches meet the ground, that is mentioned above. It can be solved by letting the arches run out of the building, but having the ends of the arches exposed to the weather then raises the issue of durability – see *Section 2.1.3*. The alternative, often used for sports stadia, is to raise the arches and use the raked seating to bring the out-thrust down to ground level *(Figure 4.10c)*.

For large-span roofs, the majority of the load is the self-weight, which is effectively uniform. But as already noted, the possibility of drifting snow on one side of the arch must be taken into account, as well as the possibility of in-plane buckling due to the use of an over-slender section. To allow for these conditions, arches should have a maximum span-to-rise ratio of 8:1, and a maximum span-to-depth ratio of 50:1, unless a detailed analysis of these secondary effects is made. Out-of-plane buckling is normally resisted by using the roof deck as a diaphragm, but the depth-to-width ratio of the arch section should be limited to around 5:1.

The large curved members which are required for arch construction can only be made from glulam. These are fabricated by the method outlined in *Section 2.3*, with the L-shaped formers set to the arch profile. The glued laminates are then pulled to the shape, and clamped until the glue has set *(Figures 4.11, 4.12)*. Transporting the sections to site must be borne in mind – the loading gauge for road transport is much more restrictive in height and width than length. A conventional three-pinned arch can be made in two sections, and transported by lorry *(Chapter 2, Figure 2.29)*.

Figure 4.10

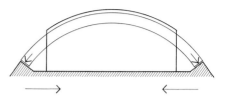

a Arch restrained by tie at ground level

b Arch in bending under asymmetric load

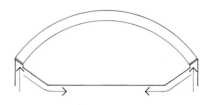

c Raised arch

Figure 4.11 *(top right)*
Curved arches in manufacture.

Figure 4.12 *(bottom right)*
Arch after planing and trimming.

The various forms of roof which can be made from arches are:

- The barrel vault
  This is formed from a series of identical arches, and overlain with a rigid deck which both stabilises the individual arches and the roof as a whole. The deck could be formed, for example, of tongue-and-grooved planking, as shown in *(Figure 4.13)*, where the planks are simultaneously the roof deck and the hall ceiling. This is probably the most economic roof form for a large-span timber structure. There is, of course, no roof void, and the main services will either be exposed as here, or dealt with in other elements of the structure.

- The dome
  This is usually formed by a series of half-arches connected to a central steel hub to form a circle *(Figure 4.14)*. It is sometimes possible to design the circumferential purlins to restrain the radial anti-thrust. For buildings which would fit better under an ellipse than a circle, such as sports stadia, arches of varying profile may be set to generate an ellipsoidal shape *(Figure 4.15)*. For very large roofs where fabrication and transportation of the elements might be difficult, 'truss arches' may be used, which can be re-assembled at site. In this case the stability of small members such as the bottom chords over the large span would need careful engineering.

- The portal
  This is essentially an arch which has been distorted to conform more to the building's shape of walls and roof. As a consequence, it has to resist significant bending as well as compression forces. Architecturally it is an impressive form *(Figure 4.16)*. Transportation requirements will almost certainly require the section to be jointed, and the relatively high curvature at the knuckle will require thinner laminates to be used, increasing production costs. Laminate thicknesses should not be more than 1/250th the radius of curvature.

Figure 4.13 *(below right)*
Glulam arches, spanning 43 m, over the pool in the Littledown Sports Centre, Bournemouth.
Architect: *Saunders Architects*

Figure 4.14 *(below left)*
Spherical dome at Center Parcs, Sherwood Forest. A 70 m span of half-arches connected to a central steel node.
Client: *Center Parcs*

Figure 4.15
Ellipsoidal dome at Salzburg Arena, Austria, using glulam half-arches of varying span.
Architect: SP Engel & Zimmermann

Figure 4.16 *(below)*
Olympic pool in Sunderland. Portal frames which meet over the central roof-light.
Fabricator: Finnforest Merk

Figure 4.17
Children's climbing frame, illustrating the principle of a geodesic structure.
Fabricator/photo: Cowley Timberwork

Figure 4.18 *(right)*
Geodesic barrel vault at Portcullis House.
Architect: Michael Hopkins & Partners;
Engineer: Arup

4.1.3 Geodesic structures

Geodesic structures essentially extend the principles of triangulation into three dimensions, forming curved (or, more strictly, multifaceted) surfaces which enclose space *(Figure 4.17)*. The design is dominated by the node details – perhaps five or six members meeting at varying angles – and it is generally necessary to use metal components. The form may be a regular geometrical shape, such as a dome or a cylinder. For the atrium roof in Portcullis House at Westminster *(see Case Study 12)* a barrel vault with hipped ends cover a space 50 m x 25 m *(Figure 4.18)*, with the node connections shown in *Chapter 3, Figure 3.09*. The timber members are formed from glulams in American white oak. The information necessary to fabricate all the different node conditions came from a computer model of the roof geometry, which in 2000 anticipated a decade of advancement in the role of computers for complex geometric structures *(see Chapter 5)*.

The most efficient structural form is the dome, which has been used for some of the largest timber roofs. The dome at the Royal Agricultural Halls, Sydney, erected for the 2002 Olympics *(Figure 4.19)* is 100 m in diameter, with glulam members connected to a simple steel end plate in compression. The roof of Marlowe Academy in Ramsgate *(Figure 4.20)* is part of a toroid (or doughnut) although the basic form is adapted to give a larger vertical radius for the inner section. The connection detail is shown in *Chapter 3, Figure 3.09g*.

Figure 4.19
Sydney Showground Olympic Hall.
Architect: *Ancher, Mortlock and Wooley;*
Engineer: *Arup*

a *(left)*
100 m diameter geodesic dome, with a central steel ring.

b *(above)*
Base shoe.

Figure 4.20
Marlowe Academy at Ramsgate, Kent. A geodesic dome of simple Kerto members with Cowley connectors into steel nodes.
Architect: *BDP;*
Engineer: *BDP and Capita Symonds;*
Timber engineer: *BDP and Capita Symonds*

Figures 4.21, 4.22
Lockhart lecture theatre at Napier University, Edinburgh. A geodesic egg-shaped auditorium.
Architect and engineer: BDP;
Timber engineers: Symonds Group and Cowley Timberwork

Free forms are also possible, with computer definition of the shape being more or less essential. Shapes are at their most efficient when curvatures in both directions are positive (eg dome-like). Situations that call for careful analysis include opposing curvatures (eg a saddle shape), areas of relative flatness, and large openings. The Lockhart Lecture Theatre at Napier University, Edinburgh (*Figures 4.21, 4.22*) is an egg-shaped geodesic frame, with a very large window giving views over the city. Nodes are made of cylindrical steel billets with Cowley connectors in the timber members as for the Marlowe Academy roof. The panoramic window opening is stabilised by the window mullions, which do double duty as strut elements of the frame.

4.1.4 Lamella structures

The lamella roof made its appearance in Germany in 1921 in a system patented by Friedrich Zollinger. The aim was to construct arch roofs using relatively short timber members, which interlocked to create a cylindrical surface (*Figure 4.23*). All members are identical and two modules long, with a central mortice and two end tenons. Like the gridshell, the rectangular system needs to be stabilised, either by triangulating members or by an overlying deck. Initially used for house roofs, it was later applied to larger structures with a span of 30 m or more, although few examples now exist. It essentially forms an arch, which of course is primarily in compression, with secondary bending from asymmetric loading such as drifted snow.

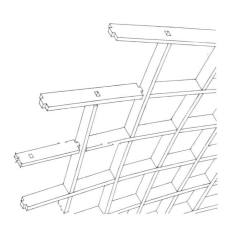

Figure 4.23
Principle of the lamella roof .

The form was revived in about 1990 and used for the Öko-Centrum, an Ecological Centre in Hamm, Germany. The roof was a series of barrel vaults some 7 m wide, spanning 13 m (*Figure 4.24*). The lamellae are 200 mm deep, and the contractor elected to cut them from curved glulam lengths, rather than from solid timber. The roof was simple to erect – falsework arches supported the node points until a vault was complete, when the arches could be moved to the next bay (*Figure 4.25*). The vault was then sheathed in Kerto (*see Section 2.3*), using gunned nails (*Figure 4.26*). Kerto can be supplied in lengths up to 25 m, and these single lengths avoid the jointing problems of

standard plywood sheets. The roof could have been designed as a simple arch spanning between the valley beams, which in consequence would have been large. By taking design advantage of composite action between the lamellae and the Kerto, the roof effectively became a shell structure, needing a valley beam of only nominal size.

In 2003, Acanthus Lawrence and Wrightson Architects, with the engineers Buro Happold, used the lamella form as a two-way spanning ribbed deck (ie working primarily in bending, with only secondary compression) over Hounslow East station *(Figure 4.27)*. In 2006 Nicolas Grimshaw Architects, with SKM Anthony Hunt as engineers, designed the large roof over the Core project at the Eden Centre *(Figures 4.28, 4.29)*. The structure is based on contra-rotating spirals with a layout based on the Fibonacci series (better known as the pattern of a sunflower seedhead). Each lamella is in double curvature, and the ends are connected to achieve continuity of the structure as a whole, using steel plates in end slots with dowel connections *(Figure 4.29)*.

An entertaining use of the lamella principle was seen briefly at the Serpentine Pavilion of 2008 *(Figure 4.30)* and is also described in *Section 5.5*.

4.1.5 The gridshell

The history of the gridshell can be traced back to the seventeenth century when Robert Hooke, the mathematician and engineer, stated that 'a hanging chain (working in tension only), inverted, will form a stable arch (working in compression only)'. Determining the optimum geometry for arches by inverting the shapes taken by hanging chains, subsequently became a technique much used in the field of heavyweight materials – for instance the design of masonry arches. The Spanish architect Antoni Gaudi extended the idea to three dimensions in the late nineteenth century, by using a hanging net model to determine the thrust lines of vaults for a projected church in Barcelona.

Figure 4.24 *(top left)*
Roof at Öko-Centrum, Hamm, Germany. Seven lamella barrel vaults.
Engineer: Arup

Figure 4.25 *(top middle)*
Öko-Centrum: erection of falsework.

Figure 4.26 *(bottom left)*
Kerto decking in single lengths.

Figure 4.27 *(right)*
Lamella roof to Hounslow East underground station. Kerto elements on a two-way span.
Architect: Acanthus Lawrence and Wrightson;
Engineers: Buro Happold and SKM Anthony Hunt

Figure 4.30 *(bottom middle)*
Serpentine Summer Pavilion 2005, London *(see Case Study 5.5)*.
Architects: Alvaro Siza and Eduardo Souto de Moura;
Engineers: Arup and Cecil Balmond

Figure 4.28 *(below)*
'The Core' roof at the Eden
Centre. Lamella roof
with continuity at the lamella
ends, giving a two-way
spanning deck.
Architect: *Nicholas Grimshaw*
and Partners;
Engineers: *Buro Happold and*
SKM Anthony Hunt

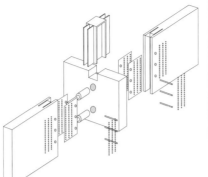

Figure 4.31
Frei Otto's 15 m diameter dome – the first gridshell.
Photo: *Stuttgart University*

Figure 4.29 *(right)*
'The Core' roof: exploded
detail of flitch joint.

From 1946 Professor Frei Otto of Stuttgart University experimented with hanging chain models of uniform square grids, pin-jointed at the connections. In simple terms, such a net could be hung to develop a saucer-like depression, with the peripheral squares distorting to diamond shapes. If the net was then 'inverted' (by, for example, looking into a mirror below the net) the result would be a 'dome' which, on Hooke's original principle, could resist a uniform gravity load in pure compression, as long as it had a peripheral restraint. Frei Otto's first full-scale structure was a 15 m diameter dome made of 40 mm x 100 mm pine laths bolted together at 0.48 m centres, with a centre height of 5.0 m *(Figure 4.31)*. To make the structure more resistant to point and non-uniform loads, the bolted connections were then tightened. The laths are subject to considerable internal bending forces as they are pulled to the required profile, and it was found that the timber had to be of high quality, or it fractured at the knots.

An opportunity to use this system on a larger scale came with an appointment to design the Pavilion for the first International Garden Festival at Mannheim in 1975, with Ove Arup and Partners as engineers. The building has a complex plan shape *(Figure 4.32)*, and the larger hall has a diameter of around 40 m. Initial calculations showed that a single lattice would not be stiff enough to resist local loading. If the laths were simply made deeper, it

would not be possible to bend them to the required radii, and so the design was based on a double lattice of 50 mm x 50 mm members, connected by bolts in slotted holes to allow for one lattice to slide over the other as the final shape was formed *(Figure 4.33)*.

The laths were made from high grade hemlock (ie with small knots and straight grain). Individual pieces were finger-jointed together to make lengths some 30 m long, which were then jointed on site with nailed lapped pieces. The curvature of the laths for the Multi-halle (expressed as the thickness divided by the bent radius) was only around 1/800, but much tighter radii (about 1/300) were required for the connecting tunnels. Occasional breakages were repaired with lapping pieces as before.

The entire grid was assembled flat on the ground floor, and gradually lifted into position, stabilised at intermediate stages by propping it on scaffold towers *(Figure 4.34)*. The bolts were then tightened, with spring washers to take up any residual drying shrinkage in the timber. Increased stiffness in critical areas was obtained with blocking pieces bolted between the upper and lower laths (making the effective structural depth 150 mm rather than 50 mm), and adding some diagonal steel ties. The whole structure was then covered with a membrane, which was estimated to have a twenty-year life.

Figure 4.32 *(left)*
Mannheim Garden Festival gridshell.
Photo: Arup

Figure 4.33 *(middle)*
Mannheim Garden Festival gridshell lattice detail. Four timber layers and triangulating cables.
Photo: Arup

Figure 4.34 *(right)*
Mannheim Garden Festival gridshell during erection. The towers were progressively lifted by fork lift truck, and then underbuilt, in a process which would be unlikely to satisfy modern health and safety assessments.
Photo: Arup

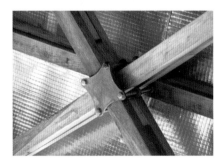

Figure 4.35 *(top)*
Weald and Downland Museum gridshell. The bending of the shell complete.
Architect: Edward Cullinan Architects;
Engineer: Buro Happold;
Photo: Green Oak Carpentry Company

Figure 4.36 *(centre)*
Weald and Downland. Interior view – cladding battens and roof-light.

Figure 4.37 *(bottom)*
Weald and Downland. Node detail.

Although the membrane was recently renewed, the structure still stands today, some 35 years after completion.

The Mannheim Pavilion established the general principles of large-scale grid-shell construction, which were:

- Finger-jointed laths of high-grade timber.

- A double-layer rectangular grid.

- Node connectors which would allow initial rotation and slip of the members, but which could then be tightened.

- Blocking pieces between the layers to increase the strength under local loading (such as maintenance access or drifting snow).

- Additional stabilisation of the grid by means of triangulating members, or a rigid roof covering.

The Pavilion showed that the grid-shell had structural potential, as well as being a visually exciting form.

In the UK the first major gridshell to be constructed was the workshop and display building at the Weald and Downland Museum *(Case Study 11)*. It is smaller than Mannheim, but more ambitious in its form *(Figure 4.35)*. The curvature varies, but is generally tighter than Mannheim, down to a maximum of around 1/200. The lath depth was reduced to 35 mm, and the oak used green rather than dry, giving greater flexibility. Finger-jointing the laths with conventional formaldehyde glues (which require dry timber) would not have been feasible, so a polyurethane-based glue was used. The grid was gradually pulled down to profile in stages over a period of six weeks, although a few fractures occurred at the positions of tightest curvature. The shell is stabilised by means of horizontal battens which triangulate the structure generally, and provide fixing lines for the covering *(Figures 4.36, 4.37)*.

In 2006 another major gridshell was constructed at the Savill Gardens in Windsor Great Park *(Case Study 10)*. Again it was doubly curved, with an undulating ridge, but was overall much flatter than Weald and Downland, which meant that it was relatively easy to bend the lower lattice to profile *(Figures 4.38, 4.39)*. The shear blocks between the lattices had been pre-fixed, ready for the top lattice to be put in position. Since the construction of the elements was sequential, all connections could be made simply by machine-driven screws.

In this case the shell was stabilised by an overlay of plywood, which acted as a deck for the roof construction, and the ceiling of the building, *(Figure 4.40)*.

4.1.6 Stressed skin structures

Many roofs and floors are made up of a series of joists with a deck above and a ceiling below, neither of which directly contribute to joist strengths. If, however, they have continuity in themselves, and are rigidly connected to the joists acting as flanges, a very considerable increase in strength and

Figure 4.38 *(above)*
Savill Gardens gridshell. Assembling the lower layer of the grid.
Architect: *Glenn Howells Architects;*
Engineer: *Buro Happold*

Figure 4.39 *(top left)*
Savill Gardens. Fixing the upper laths.
Photo: *Green Oak Carpentry Company*

Figure 4.40 *(left)*
Savill Gardens. View of deck from below.

stiffness results through 'box action'. A rigid connection in this context means glue – the efficiency of mechanical connections is always reduced due to slip, and as noted earlier, glueing large components requires factory conditions. Thus the decision to use stressed skin panels is essentially balanced between structural efficiency and the practicalities of manufacture, transport and erection.

In 2001 Hodder Associates, with Arup, designed a swimming pool at Darleston with a roof of stressed skin panels *(Figure 4.41)*. Essentially made up of a series of deck beams of long lengths, and of widths to suit transport requirements, it is a very light structure for its span, and provides both the deck for the roof covering and the pool ceiling *(Figure 4.42)*.

Figure 4.41 *(right)*
Darleston pool. Prefabricated roof unit.
Architect: *Hodder Associates;*
Engineer: *Arup;*
Fabricator/photo: *Cowley Timberwork*

Figure 4.42 *(above)*
Darleston pool. Prefabricated roof unit. The completed pool, with the bottom flange of the units forming the ceiling.

4.2 Frames

Introduction
An all-timber building frame is a more challenging task for a designer, particularly if the decision is taken to expose the frame members. The principal design issues are:

- Architectural texture.

- Fire resistance.

- Stability.

- Service accommodation.

Architectural texture
While roofs are generally seen at long range, an open timber frame can often be within touching distance, and the architectural texture of the surfaces becomes very significant *(Figure 4.44)*. The texture is a function of:

Figure 4.43
Close view of the arches at Littledown Sports Centre *(see Figure 4.13)* **on the rear gallery.**

- The surface figure. This is revealed as the saw intercepts the growth rings of the tree. For larger members there will be also be the grading 'defects' – principally knots. Timber installed 'green' will show some degree of splitting, and glulam beams will show the laminate lines and their finger joints *(Figure 4.43)*.

- The method of conversion. This might range from a coarse circular or band saw, with the inevitable roughness which they produce, to fine sawing, where the teeth marks are only just discernible. Planing, of course, produces a 'plane' surface, but does enable the figure to be seen to best advantage.

- Finish. With all these visual advantages, timber needs little in the way of applied finishes – the most usual choice is a transparent timber sealer, particularly in areas of potential hand contact, as finely prepared surfaces are irresistible to the touch. If the building is of vernacular form, the timber is often left unfinished, and the surface will develop a natural patina of use – see *Case Study 18* of the Globe Theatre. It is nevertheless possible to apply a conventional paint scheme.

Figure 4.44
Accordia flats, Cambridge *(see Case Study 21)* **Green oak frame supporting balconies, itself stabilised from the main block.**

Figure 4.45
House at Rowe Lane, Hackney. Frame construction, with moment-resisting joints and no diagonals.
Architect: *Marcus Lee Architects;*
Engineer: *Arup*

Fire resistance

Unlike roofs, frames will generally require some period of fire resistance - usually 30 minutes, or occasionally up to an hour, depending on the scale of the building. There are two ways of achieving fire resistance:

- Cover the timber with fire-resisting material. This method is generally used for modern domestic construction, using plasterboard or other non-combustible linings.

- Size the timber so that it has sufficient cross-sectional area to retain integrity for the required period, as noted in *Section 2.4.1*. However, it is obvious that for light softwood members (say 75 mm or less in thickness) protection is the only way forward.

Stability

All frames must have sufficient strength (against falling down) and stability (against falling over). Stability may be achieved by:

- Connection to an adjacent structure. The balconies at Accordia *(Case Study 21) (Figure 4.44)* are an open frame of green oak, which is stabilised by its attachment to the main block.

- Triangulation. This is the principle shown in most of the roof and truss systems described so far, and used in historic framed structures.

- Rigid connections. These are more difficult to detail, in terms of stiffness as well as strength, but avoid the spatial restrictions sometimes caused by triangulating members, *(Figure 4.45)*.

- Stiff racking panels. These can be overlaid, or incorporated within the panels of the structure.

Service accommodation

The more exposed the frame is, the more thought must be given to service accommodation – in particular the larger elements such as ventilation ducts. The options include:

- Allowing the service runs to stand exposed, and designing the casings with this in mind – as an example see *Figure 4.13*.

- Centralising the services in framed shafts with removable infill panels.

4.2.1 Post and beam frames (dry material)

Post and beam frames much above domestic scale are generally fabricated in softwood glulam. The discipline of beams on posts often produces a plan of grid form, although there is no reason why this should be strictly repetitive or rectangular. The new Faculty of Education at Cambridge University *(Figure 4.46)* is set out to a curved plan, where lines of twin beams grasp the posts and carry the floor joists. All members are sized for one-hour fire resistance and all metal connectors are recessed and plugged.

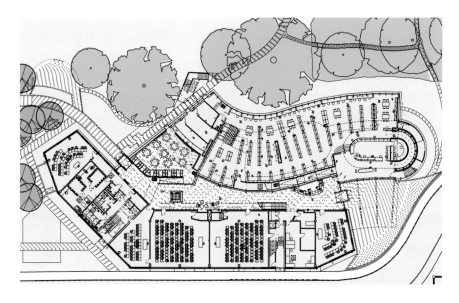

Figure 4.46
Faculty of Education, Cambridge.
Floor plans.
Drawing: BDP

The house at Rowe Lane, Hackney, uses a frame in larch, exposed both inside and out, with moment-resisting joints *(Figure 4.45)* achieved by the use of Cowley Connectors *(see Section 3.3.2)*. The thermal insulation value of timber prevents the posts from acting as cold bridges. Mossbourne Academy *(Case Study 17)*, one of the largest frames constructed in recent years, is based on a series of H-frames and cross-beams, and is also one of the very few buildings to use composite construction for the floors (concrete floor slabs bonded to timber cross-beams).

Figure 4.47
Chithurst Buddhist Monastery, West Sussex. Frame in green oak.
Framers: Green Oak Carpentry Company

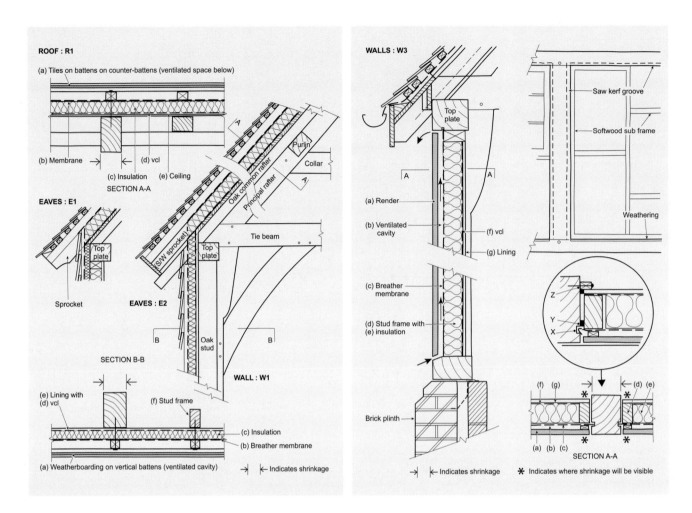

Figure 4.48
Two variants of timber frame construction in green oak.

a *(left)*
the whole of the external envelope is located outside the frame, which means that the frame is visible only from inside the building

b *(right)*
the cladding, insulation, and internal finish are all within the zone of the posts, which means that the frame is visible from both inside and out

4.2.2 Traditional framing (using green material)

Today we routinely specify dry timber for construction, but there are good reasons for using green timber for post and beam structures, which are given in *Section 3.1*. Since the frame is going to dry out in service, the joints shown there have, on Darwin's principle of survival of the fittest, shown over time that they are capable of keeping their integrity over this period.

Traditional frame forms are also a useful reference because the member sizes lie within the normal range of commercial supply. The frame for Chithurst Monastery *(Figure 4.47)* is based on a traditional barn form, albeit with some very 20th century fenestration.

The effect of drying movements should also be considered in relation to frame cladding. The most reliable solution is to detail the whole of the external envelope (that is the weather boarding and the insulation) outside the frame. This solution means that the frame is visible only from inside the building *(Figure 4.48a)*. To see the frame from both inside and out requires setting the cladding, insulation, and internal finish within the zone of the posts *(Figure 4.48b)*, in which case care must be taken to avoid the post-shrinkage opening up of leakage paths.

There is, of course, no reason why structures in contemporary style may not be successfully built using green oak – as for instance at Bedales School, Surrey *(Figure 4.49)* or Darwin College, Cambridge *(Figure 4.50)*, and the principles of design could also be applied to frames of chestnut, Douglas fir, or larch, all available in larger sections.

4.2.3 Platform frame construction

The history of the modern timber frame begins in Chicago in the mid-nineteenth century, with the invention of the 'balloon' frame, so-called because its erection was said to be 'as easy as blowing up a balloon'. The analogy was questionable, but the name stuck. In essence, the heavy framing techniques outlined in the previous sections were abandoned in favour of frames of small-section timber, all held together with a very large bag of the new mass-produced nails. Given the generous supplies of timber available in the States, the external panels were two storeys high. When the system arrived in the UK, these timbers were difficult to source, and the system was changed to single-storey panels throughout in what became known as 'platform frame construction' – the floor deck becomes the platform for the next storey.

Figure 4.49
Bedales School theatre, Surrey. Corner of auditorium.
Architect: *Feilden Clegg Bradley Architects;*
Engineers: *Ian Duncan, Structures One;*
Fabricator/photo: *Green Oak Carpentry Company*

Figure 4.50 *(left)*
Darwin College, Cambridge, Study Centre. Drying fissures in post.

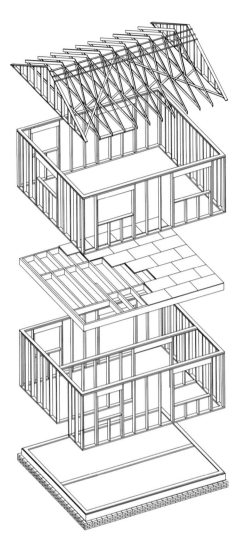

Figure 4.51
Timber-framed housing: factory-made panels assembled on site by crane.

Nearly all the timber-framed housing built since the 1960s uses this system, based on factory-made panels assembled on site by crane *(Figures 4.51, 4.52)*. The external wall panels are covered with sheathing of, for example, OSB *(see Section 2.3)*. At this stage the internal lining of plasterboard is left off to allow installation of the services, while window and door openings are framed round. The floor might be formed of three or four cassettes – the component sizes are related to transport limitations. All connections are made by nailing. As noted in *Section 3.2* the timber frame is fire-protected throughout by a plasterboard lining.

The roof is made up of trussed rafters fabricated as described in *Section 3.2*. The whole frame can be erected in a matter of days, and is then ready for an external cladding of tiles and brickwork. As noted in *Section 2.4* the timber frame is fire protected throughout by a plasterboard lining.

Today there is growing interest in 'closed panel' construction, where insulation, services and linings are added in the factory to allow faster erection on site, and give greater air-tightness in use.

4.3 External joinery and cladding

4.3.1 Windows

Window design has changed greatly over the past few years owing to new statutory requirements for:

- Reduced heat loss from buildings. There are two requirements – lower U-values of frames and glazing; and greater air-tightness.

- Safer window cleaning in high buildings. This essentially means being able to clean windows from the inside.

These and other environmental factors have led not only to changes in window design itself, but also to a need for new window-related components such as louvres and shutters to provide shading against the sun, and the replacement of glazed opening lights by solid wood ventilation panels.

Window configuration
While traditional outward-opening windows are more common in the UK, a variety of inward-opening configurations are now frequently specified, mostly in response to stricter safety legislation on window cleaning in high-rise buildings. In addition, inward-opening windows are – unlike outward-opening ones – fully compatible with external louvres and shutters – particularly (but not only) on multi-storey buildings.

Pivot windows were used in the past to allow the outside faces of windows to be cleaned from the inside, but they tend to conflict with curtains and blinds, and can be dangerous in rotation because the upper part opens inwards and the lower half outwards. They are also subject to leaks at the pivot point. They are therefore no longer popular, and reversible windows (see below), which rotate outside the building, offer a safer alternative.

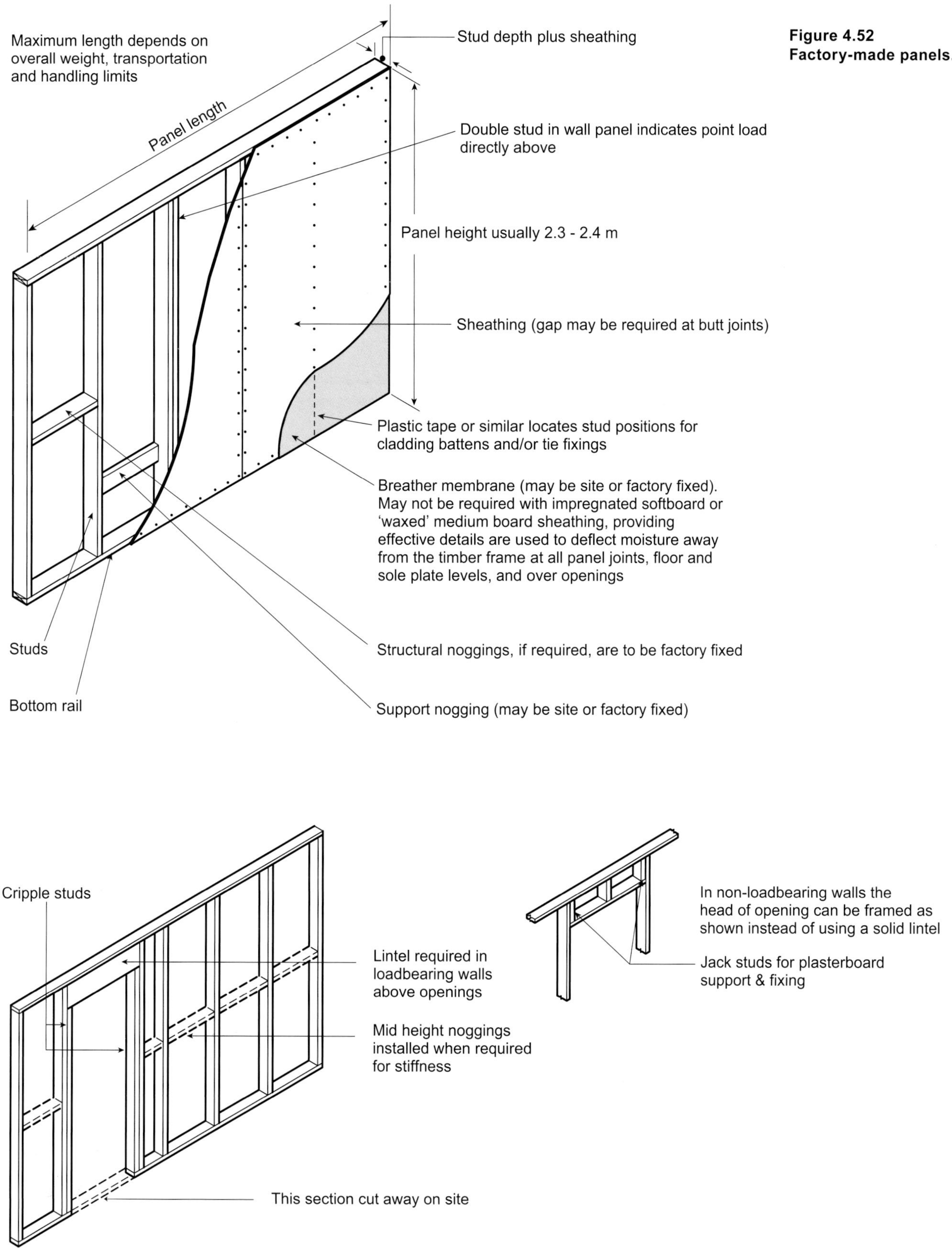

Maximum length depends on overall weight, transportation and handling limits

Panel length

Stud depth plus sheathing

Figure 4.52
Factory-made panels.

Double stud in wall panel indicates point load directly above

Panel height usually 2.3 - 2.4 m

Sheathing (gap may be required at butt joints)

Plastic tape or similar locates stud positions for cladding battens and/or tie fixings

Breather membrane (may be site or factory fixed). May not be required with impregnated softboard or 'waxed' medium board sheathing, providing effective details are used to deflect moisture away from the timber frame at all panel joints, floor and sole plate levels, and over openings

Structural noggings, if required, are to be factory fixed

Support nogging (may be site or factory fixed)

Studs

Bottom rail

Cripple studs

Lintel required in loadbearing walls above openings

Mid height noggings installed when required for stiffness

In non-loadbearing walls the head of opening can be framed as shown instead of using a solid lintel

Jack studs for plasterboard support & fixing

This section cut away on site

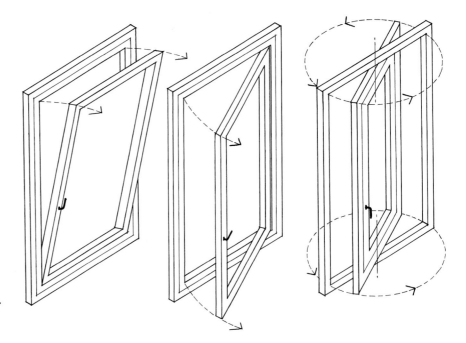

Figure 4.53
Example of a tilt-and-turn window. With the handle pointing up *(left)* the window tilts inwards for ventilation; with the handle horizontal *(centre)* it acts as an inward-opening side-hung window; with the handle pointing down *(right)* the opening light rotates 180° to allow cleaning from the inside.

The most widely-used configurations to meet current requirements are the following:

Side-hung and top-hung outward-opening windows remain popular in dwellings. Modern versions are designed to current thermal and acoustic insulation standards, and safety devices permit them to be securely held in a slightly open position for ventilation. They may not be suitable (a) for multi-storey buildings, where the need for external cleaning conflicts with safety legislation; (b) on ground floors beside a street or pathway, where the opening light might injure passers-by; or (c) in conjunction with external shutters or louvres, but where permitted they are still an economical and attractive option.

Tilt-and-turn windows are inward-opening, and therefore suitable for all three of the situations noted above. In operation *(Figure 4.53)* they are 'tilted' to provide ventilation, and 'turned' to allow cleaning from the inside. They have long been used in Scandinavia and Europe. But in Britain they are less popular in residential buildings because they conflict with curtains and blinds, and are liable to knock plants and decorative objects off internal window boards.

Reversible windows can be supplied side-hung ('side-swing') or top-hung. Both types can be turned inside-out for easy cleaning from the inside, and unlike tilt-and-turn windows they do not interfere with curtains or with objects on the window board. They are particularly suitable for high-rise office or residential blocks.

Frames and glazing

The inherent insulation properties of wood give timber window frames an advantage over other materials. But frame profiles have had to become larger than the old EJMA (English Joinery Manufacturers' Association) designs to accommodate the thicker insulated glass units (IGUs) which are needed to meet current insulation standards. Frames of the EJMA type will still be appropriate when replacing existing windows with new ones of the same appearance; but elsewhere their continued use appears to be due mostly to a belief among house builders that it is 'traditional' to the UK.

The larger frame sizes we are now seeing have in the past been resisted by the wood window industry because (it was argued) they would make timber windows more expensive, and therefore uncompetitive with plastic and aluminium frames. But now that window units are offered factory finished and glazed, weather-stripped, and fitted with sophisticated ironmongery such as espagnolette bolts, mortice locks, and complex hinges, the cost of the wood is becoming a smaller proportion of the total window cost. In cases where the timber cost remains important, the required savings could be better achieved by reducing the sub-frame sections rather than the opening lights.

The trend away from frame manufacture, glazing, and finishing as separate activities, and placing the entire contract with a single specialist window supplier, possibly including installation, brings many advantages. It is more economical; the responsibility in case of dispute then lies with one person instead of being spread across several; and the quality of manufacture, painting, glazing, and fitting ironmongery is vastly improved if these operations are carried out in the controlled conditions of a factory environment, rather than on a building site.

Fully finished windows are very compatible with the growing practice of making the openings for windows in brickwork walls with formers, and then inserting the window unit after completion of the wet trades, instead of the traditional practice of using wood window frames to form the openings in the brickwork. If frames are set into pre-formed openings in this way, there are no structural reasons for large frame sections (unless larger-span transoms or mullions are required); and if catches, locks and bolts are not surface mounted, there is no need for the sub-frames to be larger than the opening light frame sections.

Materials

In the UK most timber windows are made from treated softwood, usually European redwood *(see Sections 2.2.1 and 2.3.1,* and *Table 2.1)*, but Meranti and some other far-Eastern hardwoods are being occasionally used. European oak is becoming more frequently used for bespoke window designs, and is sometimes left unfinished to weather to grey, to avoid the need for repainting – see *Section 2.5.*

On the continent of Europe, by contrast, window frames and sub-frames have for many years been made from laminated sections, partly because the thicker insulated glass units used there require larger-section frames, and the latter can be more cheaply made from glued-together small timber sections than from frames cut from solid wood. As frame profiles in the UK become larger for the reasons given above, and as wood becomes more expensive, British manufacturers may move in the same direction, and eventually abandon the old EJMA frames.

Finishes

Modern factory-applied paints may last 8 to 10 years before requiring repainting, but on multi-storey buildings even this may be unacceptable to building owners, particularly if the repainting requires scaffolding.

This has led to the recent introduction into the UK of composite windows, which have long been popular on the continent. These windows generally have laminated softwood frames with a protective casing of aluminium on the outer face, thus combining the advantages of the insulation properties of wood; the appearance of wood on the inside; and a virtually maintenance-free external face.

For general guidance on timber finishes see *Section 2.5.*

4.3.2 External doors

Until quite recently, external doors in the UK did not have to meet any statutory requirements, whereas continental designers have for a long time had to achieve performance levels similar to windows in respect of thermal resistance, weather-tightness, and in some countries acoustic protection. Compliance with these regulations was facilitated by the general European practice of purchasing complete doorsets (i.e. door and frame) as is now universally done for windows. Obviously this practice allows an integrated design, in terms for instance of providing interlocking weather seals and increased levels of security in relation to the mounting of hinges and locks. Now that UK regulations have been revised along similar lines, it is possible that we will follow this trend.

4.3.3 Louvres

External louvres *(Figure 4.54)*, either of metal or wood, which protect areas of glazing from the sun are becoming more popular. This is perhaps more apparent in the design of larger buildings, but their use can now be seen even at domestic level. Although the passive solar heat generated by daylight entering the building through the windows is beneficial in winter, it may cause overheating in summer, and also bring problems of glare. Horizontal louvres can be designed to allow entry to low-angle winter sun, but provide shade in summer while (unlike internal blinds or curtains) keeping the solar heat out of the building.

In the simplest form, sun protection may consist only of horizontal shutters, or louvres directly across the face of the glazing. More sophisticated versions may be freestanding screens, vertically arranged across the face of the buildings, or in projecting horizontal racks shadowing the façade. These latter arrangements do not necessarily prevent the use of conventional outward-opening windows, and may also still permit window cleaning from the outside.

Sun shading devices would, until fairly recently, have made use of aluminum louvres of an aerofoil section. In more sophisticated applications these may have been adjustable in pitch, either manually or powered. The growing enthusiasm for wood among architects has resulted in many of the more recent installations using wood louvres rather than aluminium, generally

Figure 4.54
Timber louvres.

on metal support frames. Consequently even the major manufacturers of aluminium systems are now offering alternative designs in wood.

To avoid maintenance costs wood louvres are usually unfinished, and Western red cedar *(see Chapter 2, Table 2.1)* is often chosen for its natural weathering characteristics, durability and light weight. However, it is not the strongest of woods, requires care in the design of connections, and can be fairly easily damaged. Whatever species is chosen it is important that the latter should be low-movement and of a high grade, and that the section should be designed to resist the relevant wind loading. For these reasons, some of the stronger, more stable and durable tropical hardwoods from sustainable sources are now being specified for louvres.

4.3.4 Panel ventilation

Traditionally, natural ventilation has been provided to buildings by including a number of opening lights in any window or glazed wall. However, as thermal insulation standards have improved, the weight of glazing has increased, which in turn has increased frame sections and loads on hinges, particularly for large undivided windows. Even with the most efficient multiple glazing, however, the insulation of a glazed window is unlikely to achieve that of an insulated panel. If it is not necessary to have more glazing for daylight than can be provided by a fixed glass panel, ventilation can be easily provided by a hinged solid panel which may be lighter and provide better insulation than glass. In Scandinavia such a system has been popular for some time, providing an improved level of insulation when closed, and ensuring adequate controlled ventilation when open (as well as providing a higher level of security).

4.3.5 External cladding

The use of wood as an external cladding is becoming more popular, and most current installations use the material with no applied finish. The designer's aims are obviously to exploit the appeal of the natural wood surface, and to avoid or reduce the costs associated with application and maintenance of a paint coating.

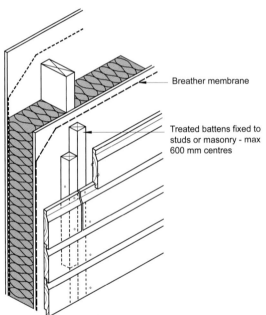

Breather membrane

Treated battens fixed to studs or masonry - max 600 mm centres

Figure 4.55
Horizontal boarding:
typical construction.

However, it must be accepted that wood exposed to the weather will gradually change its colour to a shade of grey. Wooden pleasure boats only remain a golden brown because they are regularly scraped down and re-varnished – a maintenance regime which, if applied to cladding, would be as impractical as it is expensive, although it is sometimes seen on small private houses.

The various factors which are responsible are interactive. The colour change is basically due to the action of sunlight, or more strictly its ultraviolet (UV) component, and variations in pattern can be caused by the shielding effects of overhangs or projections. The tannin, from oak in particular, is dark in colour when washed out by rain, and the total result is not completely predictable. Viewers' reactions to the ultimate weathered appearance are variable: it is accepted without question on historic buildings or historic re-creations such as the Globe Theatre *(see Case Study 18)*, and generally admired; but on modern buildings what for some is a vibrant texture, is for others an apparent lack of maintenance.

Thus the advice for designers is:

- Base the decision to use the cladding on the probable weathered appearance, rather than the natural colour of the timber.

- Consider the surface modelling, and the possible effect this will have on the consistency of the texture.

- Look at existing examples, if possible establishing the age of the installation.

At the end of this section, there are brief notes on the weathering performance of the most commonly-used timber species. The whole subject of cladding is covered in more detail in *External Timber Cladding*.

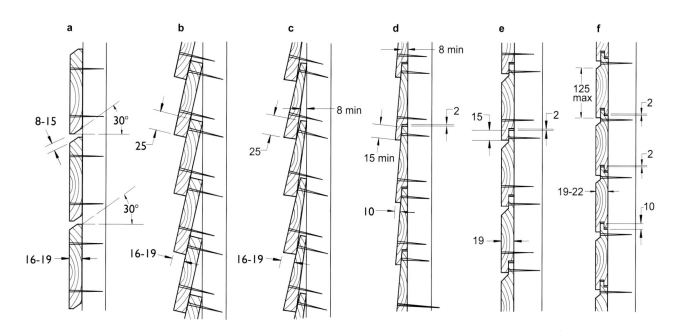

Support framing and board profiles

Horizontal boards are face-fixed to treated vertical softwood battens, set at around 600 mm centres, with a breather membrane fitted behind the battens to prevent any wind-blown moisture entering the building *(Figure 4.55)*. The vertical cavity created between the battens allows air circulation which will carry away any build-up of moisture on the rear face of the boards. The battens are shown fixed to a timber frame, but could equally well be fixed to brickwork. The boards are typically between 100 mm to 150 mm wide, and can be cut to a variety of profiles as shown in *(Figure 4.56)*. They all give different textures. Tongued and grooved and shiplap boards present the surface in a continuous plane; feather- and square-edge boards emphasise horizontal lines by virtue of the shadow from the lower edge.

Figure 4.56
Horizontal boarding: typical profiles.

a Open joint
b Square edge
c Feather edge
d Rebated feather edge
e Shiplap
f Horizontal tongue and groove

If the weather membrane is carefully detailed and installed, and drainage arrangements made at the base, it is possible to use **open joints**, *(Figure 4.56a)*. Since there is no contact between adjacent boards they will dry off rapidly after rain (but in some areas it may be prudent to install an insect screen between the boards and the battens).

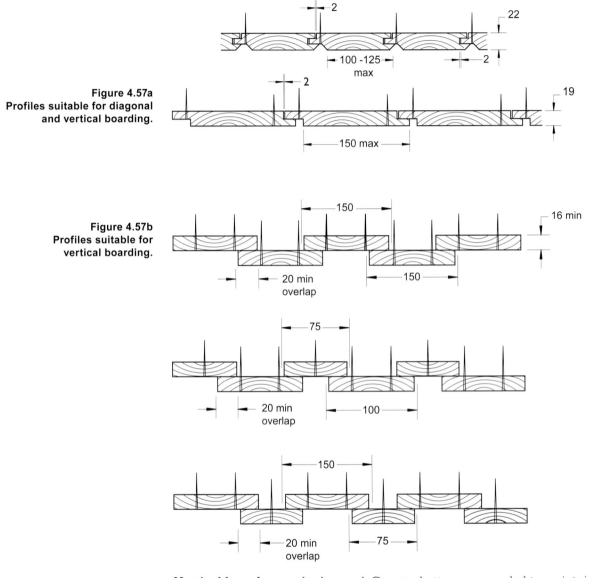

Figure 4.57a
Profiles suitable for diagonal and vertical boarding.

Figure 4.57b
Profiles suitable for vertical boarding.

Vertical boards may also be used. Counter-battens are needed to maintain air circulation, unless a board-on-board arrangement is used, which creates its own ventilation path. Vertical boards aid rapid drainage and give strong shadow lines.

Diagonal boards can create a striking chevron pattern if used in several bays.

Shingles (sawn) and **shakes** (cleft) are tapered wood pieces laid to overlap, and are fixed in the manner of slates (i.e. battens and counter-battens over a breather membrane) to walls and occasionally roofs – see the *David Douglas Pavilion, Case Study 14*.

Fasteners

As a minimum, fasteners should be galvanized, but the coating on the head may be damaged during installation. Currently, most projects use fasteners of austenitic stainless steel, which also avoids the problem of permanent staining due to the interaction of a ferrous metal with tannin. Softwood boards are normally nailed; annular ring-shank nails give an increased holding power. The temptation to use 'lost-head' nails for visual reasons should be resisted, as they may pull through under wind suction load – particularly with softer woods such as western red cedar *(see Section 2.2)*.

Hardwood boards are generally fixed with screws. Movement in the width of a hardwood board due to changes in moisture content becomes more significant, and for this reason board widths are generally limited to 150 mm, with the fasteners at the quarter points and with pre-drilled oversize holes. For green oak or chestnut, where the basic drying movements must be added to the moisture movements, washers as well as oversized holes should be specified *(Figure 4.58)*.

Figure 4.58
For green oak or chestnut washers as well as oversized holes should be specified.

Design life of untreated cladding

The design life of such claddings is difficult to predict with accuracy. Apart from the natural durability of the wood, the life would depend on:

- The elimination of sapwood, which is non-durable in all species.

- The quality of the design (ensuring water run-off).

- The quality of the installation with boards correctly gapped, fixings aligned, etc.

- The local environment (eg sheltering).

- Ease of patch repairs (eg rain-screens, which allow individual plank replacement).

The site location is also a factor, in terms of the rainfall and the driving rain index. It is not a coincidence that the majority of old timber frames are found in the east of the country.

BS 8417, after similar caveats, suggests that the design life for moderately durable softwoods, using heartwood only and not preserved, is in excess of thirty years, and for durable timber, in excess of sixty years.

Species selection

Species which are rated as 'slightly durable' and 'non-durable' *(see Chapter 2, Table 2.1)* need to be treated with preservative in order to achieve a satisfactory design life. If no applied finish, such as paint, is to be applied to the boards, then the preservative would need to chemically bond with the timber, otherwise it would leach out over time. For the higher-movement species, movement at the outer face caused by wetting and drying, is restrained by the more stable inner face, eventually resulting in the occurrence of small weathering fissures which tend to break up applied finishes.

Thus, cladding to be painted is usually made from low-movement softwood, supplied to a high grade (as knots are also prone to movement) and treated with an organic preservative. Commonly-used species are redwood and whitewood. Douglas fir (imported) and European larch, being moderately durable as long as sapwood is excluded, may be used without either a finish or preservative. Western red cedar is the only commercially available softwood which is durable.

Only a few temperate hardwoods are durable, the commercially available species being oak and sweet chestnut. As these are also high-movement timbers, they are always used without applied finishes. A considerable financial saving may be made by using these species as green material, but it is then necessary to pay special attention to the drying movements (see Section 2.1.2) both in relation to the board overlap and the fastener detail (see above).

Some tropical hardwoods are available which are fully certificated. For lesser-known species, more detailed enquiries may be needed to establish their range of properties.

Weathering performance of cladding without applied finishes

As already noted, consistency of weathering is aided by consistency of exposure. Thus installations in a single plane are less likely to show colour variation, with vertical boards giving the more rapid run-off. Significant overhangs such as deep eaves, or projecting balconies, will inevitably delay weathering of the shielded area, possibly for many years. A highly modelled façade, however, brings variation of light and shadow which can often successfully accommodate the weathering variations.

The species most commonly used are:

- Douglas fir and European larch: both are medium-density softwoods which will weather to a grey, but the stronger figure and knots in larch give a livelier texture.

- Western red cedar (imported): the only durable softwood, and probably the most favoured for cladding, all reflected in its cost. It is cut from large slow-grown trees giving a close, straight grain almost clear of knots, and weathers to a light grey.

- Oak (European): a durable hardwood, with an attractive figure. It weathers to a light grey, but the tannin which is sometimes leached out by rain creates a dark stain, which takes some time to disperse, and is variable in its effect.

4.4 External structures

The organic origin of timber makes it particularly suitable for structures of a smaller scale in a landscaped setting, such as walkways, stairs and foot-bridges. The timber is now exposed to sun and rain, and the frequent variations in surface moisture content create an increased tendency for surface fissuring to occur in species with larger movement characteristics (eg oak), which would tend to break up any applied finish, such as paint or varnish. Colour changes, to various shades of grey, are inevitable as discussed in the previous section, but a framed structure in the open weathers relatively quickly. Many external structures, such as walkways and footbridges, are in landscaped settings, where a weathered frame fits very comfortably.

Determining the potential life of an external structure is difficult because the details of the design, already discussed for cladding, significantly affect durability; but it is probable that a well-detailed structure of durable timber with stainless steel (or equivalent) connectors, will, given appropriate maintenance, achieve a life in excess of forty years.

4.4.1 Walkways and stairs

If the walkway is elevated, or over water, it should be regarded as a structural element and the deck designed for the loading from a specific use, which could vary from a house balcony to a public thoroughfare. Usually specified as a distributed load, it is the point load that is more critical, as this could be applied to a single board, and might include small wheeled vehicles such as cleaning machines or lawn-mowers. It is also necessary to restrict deflection under load to avoid a significant trip hazard between adjacent boards. Under this loading range, the deck bearers might be spaced between 400 mm and 600 mm apart, and the planks themselves would be between 25 mm and 40 mm thick. The planks would preferably be laid at an angle to any predominant direction of travel, especially so for wheeled traffic such as bicycles.

Figure 4.59
A house balcony frame in Western red cedar, awaiting planking.

Walking routes are subject to abrasion, not only from foot traffic but from sand particles originating from, for instance, adjacent footpaths or de-icing grit. Resistance to wear has an approximate correlation with species density, and so a low density species such as Western red cedar (although durable) would only be suitable for domestic installations *(Figure 4.59)*. Even there the species is vulnerable to the feet of metal furniture. Most other softwoods are of medium density, but for heavily trafficked installations hardwoods would be more appropriate. A selection of hardwoods suitable for decking is given in *Chapter 2, Table 2.1*.

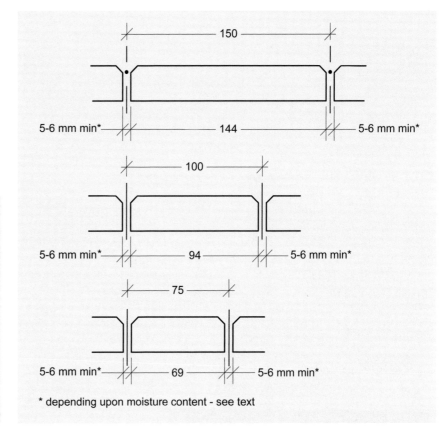

* depending upon moisture content - see text

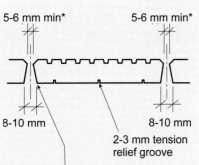

5-6 mm min*   5-6 mm min*

8-10 mm   8-10 mm

2-3 mm tension relief groove

Angle cutting either or both edges reduces risk of dirt lodging in joint

* depending upon moisture content - see text

Figure 4.60a *(right)*
Typical dimensions of decking boards without drainage grooves.

Figure 4.60b *(above)*
Typical grooved board profile. Fixings are by means of screws in 2mm oversize pre-drilled holes, positioned in grooves.

Timber surfaces, like many other materials, are slippery when covered with a layer of water, however thin. Thus the primary design aim is to drain free water from the contact surface by:

- Leaving gaps between the boards *(Figure 4.60)* These should be not less than 6mm wide, or they will hold water due to capillary action, and later, dirt. Gaps much greater than 10-12 mm might start to give problems with narrow heels or bicycle tyres. Planks installed green will shrink to some degree, and an allowance should be made for this in the spacing.

- Limiting the plank width to 150 mm.

- Grooving the upper face, thus drawing water away from the contact surface *(Figure 4.61)*. This also solves the problem of 'cupping' as the planks dry.

- If acceptable, consider a slight fall along the direction of the boards.

These are recommendations for flat areas. For ramps and stairs (i.e. areas of increased risk), consider:

- Non-slip inserts, available either pre-installed in grooved planks, or for post-installation *(Figure 4.63)*.

- An overlay of rectangular mesh (not chicken wire), as a minimum galvanized, or preferably of stainless steel, *(Figure 4.64)*.

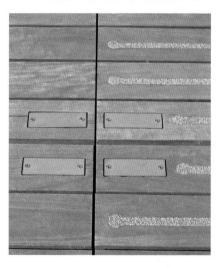

Figure 4.61 *(above)*
Decking of spaced planks with grooved upper face.

Figure 4.62a *(left)*
Deck in Paris with planed planks 150 mm wide, immediately after heavy rain. The planks, which have 'cupped up' *(see Section 4.4.1)*, retain water for a short while. 'Desire lines' (the main walking routes) have non-slip inserts.

Figure 4.62b *(bottom left)*
Detail of Paris deck. The planks are made into prefabricated panel sections by concealed screws, driven from below. Each panel may be raised for maintenance of the drainage area below by a lifting point at each corner, covered by a metal plate. The panel to the right is part of a main walking route – the planks have non-slip inserts of a gritted epoxy applied in-situ, which become very visible when the timber is wet.

Figure 4.63 *(bottom right)*
Aluminium non-slip edging strips, fixed to stair treads.

- For 'rural' structures, eg on a field path, an overlay of battens, *(Figure 4.65)*.

- For stairs and for inclined surfaces steeper than 1:20, the provision of a handrail is mandatory.

Decks in shade tend to build up algae and mould growth *(Figure 4.66)*, which increases slipperiness. They need occasional treatment with a suitable anti-fungal solution.

Fixings should preferably be of austenitic stainless steel; screws have a better holding power than nails, and can still be machine-installed. Planks over 75 mm wide should have two fixings at each bearer to prevent any 'rocking' tendency around the fixing, and the bearer width would have to accommodate two rows of screws at plank ends.

Figure 4.64
Tattershall Castle footbridge, with a galvanised mesh over old oak planks.

Figure 4.65
Battens close to a handrail on a bridge on the Thames river path.

Figure 4.66
Deck on the north side of a building, showing algae build-up in the area of less efficient surface drainage.

4.4.2 Footbridges

The most usual structural form for small to medium size bridges is shown in *Figure 4.67.* Two principal beams are linked by cross-members, which carry longitudinal joists supporting the deck, built in accordance with *Section 4.4.1.* Triangulating members ensure lateral stiffness, and connections are made with stainless steel cleats and fasteners. The principal beams will obviously be around 300 mm to 500 mm deep, and 5 m to 10 m long. Enquiries to check a source of supply may be necessary. Durable species available in large section include oak, greenheart and ekki, although timbers of these sizes will be green on delivery, and the resulting movements on drying will have to be taken into account *(see Ealing Bridge, Case Study 22).*

Figure 4.67
Two common structural arrangements for medium-span footbridges.
Based on two carriage (or principal) beams **(a),** with triangulation members **(b)** to ensure lateral rigidity. On the left-hand diagram, cross-joists **(c)** rest on the carriage beams and oversail to provide a back-stay support for the handrail posts **(d)**. Longitudinal runners **(e)** rest in turn on the cross-joists, providing support for the planks **(f).** On the right-hand diagram, cross-joists **(g)** are set between the carriage beams, with a centre runner **(h)** in turn set between them. Planks **(j)** (necessarily thicker) span between the central runner and the carriage beams. Fasteners are not shown, but are simpler for the left-hand arrangement, which has however a greater structural depth.

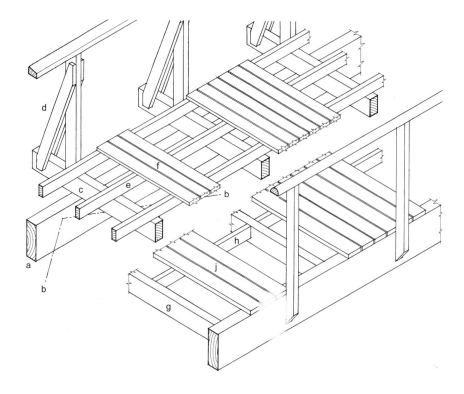

Figure 4.68
Examples of structural forms for longer span bridges.
Trusses (assembled for instance in accordance with *Chapter 3, Figure 3.08*) can support the bridge from below, as on the left hand side, with a deck for instance as shown in *Figure 4.67*, left hand side. On the right, the trusses are set as upstands, doubling as parapets, with a deck (for instance as shown in *Figure 4.67*, right hand side) between the bottom flanges. The latter arrangement minimises the structural depth, but requires more detailed consideration of the truss stability. In the lower diagram an arch is formed from three straight members, and stabilised by connections between the central member and the deck beams.

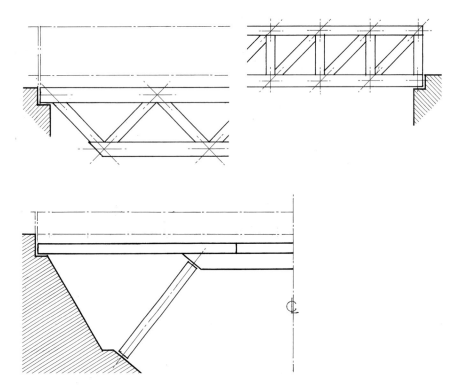

In considering the use of preservatives as an alternative to natural durability, it would be necessary (for solid timber) to check the restriction in length imposed by the treatment tanks. If a glulam is made of made from preserved laminates, much of the treated 'shell' is planed off in the course of fabrication. It is therefore preferable to pressure-treat the finished section if possible.

A further option is to protect the principal members from rain, allowing the use of moderately durable timber in glulam form without preservative. This could be done by constructing a solid deck, but the details are difficult to achieve in the context of a timber structure. Local protection to the principals by, for example, an oversailing metal cap, with a water repellant applied to the sides is possible, but the maintenance of this coating, in a bridge context, is often difficult.

The more usual forms for larger spans involve the construction of trusses or arches, *(Figure 4.68)*. The trusses are most easily positioned below the deck or, if headroom does not permit, arranged as perimeter upstands doing double duty as parapets. Consideration would then have to be given to the stability of the top flange, which is in compression. Trusses built up from relatively short members might use the connections shown in *Chapter 3, Figure 3.08*.

Arches formed from curved members would need enquiries to find a source of supply. An alternative would be a 'trussed arch' using two straight lengths with the main compression load passed between members in end contact.

5

Innovation

Peter Ross & Andrew Lawrence

This chapter looks at new forms of timber, and new ways of using timber. These include the development of modified wood for increased durability without the need for chemical preservatives; case examples of the use of timber for an eight-storey building frame, for fast-track construction, and for over-roofing large spaces such as supermarkets; and an example of the seamless use of computers from CAD to CAM without ever touching paper.

The Stadhaus, London
Photo: Will Pryce

Since the publication of 'Timber in Construction' (see the Introduction) a quarter of a century ago, there have been many significant technical innovations which have now passed into mainstream usage. These include LVL, metal web, and I- joists and cross-laminated timber *(see Section 2.3)*. The assembly times of components have also been greatly reduced by a new generation of machine-installed nails and screws. But perhaps the most significant advance overall (as in most branches of construction) has been in the exponential growth of computer power, and the range of its applications.

The earliest major use of the computer in timber engineering, dating back to the 1960s, was to design trussed rafters, with the basic analysis programme extended to produce material and cutting schedules. Later, designers used computers to create accurate three-dimensional models of structures (CAD, or computer-aided design), while fabricators have used them to guide the tools which produced structural components (CAM, or computer-aided manufacture).

The innovations for a chapter written in 2009 are somewhat different. Only two (in the field of durability) relate to processes – see *Section 5.1*. Others concern timber construction forms or techniques applied in fields which hitherto have been seen as the preserve of steel, which is the alternative framing material – see *Sections 5.2* to *5.4*. The final innovation links CAD and CAM in a single production process – see *Section 5.5*.

5.1 Alternatives to chemical preservatives

A glance at *Chapter 2, Table 2.1* shows that the softwoods which are in general use because of their low cost also have low natural durability. As an alternative to the use of the higher-priced, more durable species, preservatives were developed which impregnated the timber with toxic chemicals *(see Section 2.6)*. But, as noted in that section, the use of such preservatives is becoming increasingly restricted on the grounds of environmental pollution, both in service and end-of-life disposal.

Wood, as an organic material, has a complex structure, but is composed basically of cellulose, hemicellulose, and lignin *(see Section 2.1.1)*. One does not need to be a chemist to see that it is a potential food source, but nature has linked the constituents so effectively that only a handful of insects and fungi have found a way of breaking down the wood fibre to extract the basic nutrients. Unfortunately, the spores of these fungi are present everywhere in the atmosphere, and can land on exposed timber. To germinate, they need:

- Oxygen (also present everywhere)

- Moisture

- A food source.

Wood inside a soundly-constructed weather envelope should not contain enough moisture for germination, which is why we do not in general have durability problems inside a building. Timber exposed externally, however, will often rise above the threshold moisture value, with the consequent risk of rot development. As an alternative to chemical preservation, research has focused on eliminating – or at least reducing – the available nutrients, or reducing the potential moisture content. There is a growing number of modified woods, of which ThermoWood® and Accoya® are the most widely used in the UK at this time.

ThermoWood ®

ThermoWood® is a registered trademark name owned by the Finnish ThermoWood® Association, and is applied to heat-treated wood produced according to a methodology developed by the Technical Research Centre of Finland (VTT). The material is heated to a temperature of at least 180°C while protected with steam, over a period of some 36 hours. This causes several changes to take place in the material structure, principally the thermic degrade of the hemicelluloses, so that after treatment the fungi-susceptible material is significantly lower, giving improved resistance to decay. In addition, the tendency of the wood to absorb water decreases, which both discourages fungal growth and reduces the tendency to shrink and swell under conditions of varying moisture content.

The result is to make the material more durable and stable in an external environment. There is a darkening in colour, and some loss of strength. Thus the principal applications are for cladding, external joinery and decking, as well as for garden furniture. The appearance of ThermoWood®, after some eighteen months of exposure at the Tesco Superstore at Wick, is shown in *Figures 5.4.6, 5.4.7.*

Since nothing has been added to the material there are – in contrast to chemically preserved materials – no restrictions on service use, or end-of-life disposal. The cost of ThermoWood® in *Chapter 2, Table 2.1* would be 'medium'.

The manufacturer claims that the treated wood can be regarded as 'durable' *(see Section 2.1.3)*; but it must be remembered that – as for all materials – the prediction of a service life is necessarily based on accelerated tests, with artificially stringent conditions. It is always difficult to calibrate these results with real-life effects. Boiling an egg does not produce a chicken. This claim should therefore be treated with caution until more case study evidence is available.

Accoya ®

The technology behind Accoya® wood is based on the acetylation process, in which the wood reacts with acetic anhydride, derived from acetic acid (known in its dilute form as vinegar). Wood contains an abundance of chemical groups called 'free hydroxils', which absorb and release water according to the relative humidity of the surrounding atmosphere. This action causes the moisture movements described in *Section 2.1.2.* It is also believed that fungal decay is initiated at the free hydroxil sites.

Acetylation effectively changes the free hydroxils within the timber to hydroxyl groups, which greatly reduces the ability of the wood to absorb water. The consequences are that the wood is rendered more dimensionally stable under varying moisture conditions, and the effective reduction in moisture content substantially reduces the susceptibility to fungal attack.

The manufacturers claim that Accoya® can be regarded as 'very durable' (i.e. equivalent to teak) but again the caveat in relation to long-term predictions applies.

5.2 A nine-storey residential building in timber: Stadthaus, Murray Grove, London

Figure 5.2.1 *(above)*
View of the completed building.
Photo: Will Pryce

Figure 5.2.2 *(top middle)*
Plan of the 5th floor.
Drawing: Waugh Thistleton Architects

Figure 5.2.3 *(bottom middle)*
Pre-cut panels in the KLH factory, Austria.
Photo: Waugh Thistleton Architects

Figure 5.2.5 *(top right)*
The completed structure, before the installation of services and finishes.
Photo: Will Pryce

Figure 5.2.6 *(bottom right)*
A living room, with corner balcony.
Photo: Will Pryce

In recent years frames have explored the possibility of erecting building structures higher than the historic four-storey limit, recently lifted to seven storeys in the relevant part of the timber code. The conventional construction form *(shown in Chapter 4, Figure 4.54)* becomes more critical with height, as the local compression under the wall studs increases on the bottom rail, and the cumulative vertical movements which result from around 300 mm of cross-grain timber per storey in the load path affect, for instance, the horizontal alignments of the floors with staircases and lift thresholds.

At Stadthaus, near Old Street station in East London, the design team of Waugh Thistleton, architects, with their engineers, Techniker, have not only put forward a new approach to multi-storey timber construction but have successfully built a nine-storey prototype *(Figure 5.2.1)*, of which eight are in timber.

The ground floor level is in concrete, to accommodate the non-typical wall layout needed for plant and service rooms. Above this level, the architects designed a layout, repeated on eight levels, which gives each flat a corner balcony. These eight storeys are constructed in timber, but are not framed in the conventional manner. They were built using panels of cross-laminated timber *(see Section 2.3.5)*, fabricated in Austria and assembled by the UK contractor as a platform frame. Since this material is effectively solid timber, it brings with it a considerable increase in strength and dimensional stability. To obtain the necessary wind stability from a relatively lightweight building, most of the walls are both load-bearing and wind-resisting, which has avoided the need for significant tension restraints.

Overturning resistance derives primarily from the 'box' effect of the external wall, with some contribution from internal walls around the stairs and lift shaft *(Figure 5.2.2)*.

The panels comprise five laminations and are typically 120 mm thick. They were cut by KLH in Austria using CNC machines *(Figure 5.2.3)*, and their accuracy is such as to allow a straight butt joint between wall and floor members *(Figure 5.2.4)*. Wall panels are connected to each other by a half lap and screw detail, and to the floors above and below by metal cleats *(Figure 5.2.5)*. The solid nature of both walls and floors permits the achievement of sound insulation values better than the minimum requirements. The required period of fire resistance *(see Section 2.4)* is achieved by plasterboard protection, just as in conventional frames.

At eight storeys, this system is well within its capacity structurally, but there remains the issue of vertical movement. The depth of cross-grain timber at each storey is much reduced (being only the floor thickness of 120 mm) and the solidity of the floor slab will combine to give only very small moisture-induced movements. The external cladding is a patterned system of Eternit tiles, which readily absorbs small vertical movement of the structure.

The lift shaft is made up of three prefabricated 'tubes' butted end-to-end, so that vertical movement is essentially eliminated. The shaft is lined externally with insulation, and enclosed with load-bearing walls which are part of the general system – an arrangement that gives useful sound insulation to the lift. Owing to differential settlement between lift shaft and floors, some small adjustments may be necessary over the first year or so at the lift thresholds on the upper floors.

The staircase flights are in steel and were craned into place as prefabricated elements. Services are distributed vertically in protected ducts, and horizontally above a shallow suspended ceiling. Underfloor heating is fitted throughout, giving clean walls *(Figure 5.2.4)*.

Although there is obviously more timber in the structure than a conventional frame, the system offers simplicity and speed of construction. Erection proceeded at one storey a week, and the walls and floors of a storey could actually be erected in three days. The site was very constricted, and so the delivery of panels was related to the erection sequence, which almost eliminated the need for site storage. Overall the client/contractor Telford Homes reports some three months' saving in time over more conventional construction.

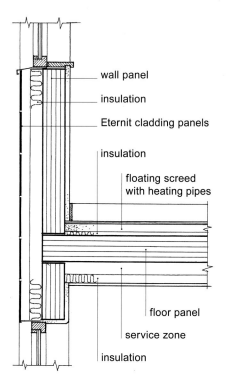

Figure 5.2.4
Cross section of the structure.
Drawing: Waugh Thistleton Architects

Awards

Wood Awards 2008
   Categories: Structural and
   off-site construction

Credits

Client/owner and main contractor
   Telford Homes plc

Architect
   Waugh Thistleton Architects

Structural engineer
   Techniker Ltd

Timber supplier
   KLH, Austria

Figure 5.3.1 *(top left)*
View of the completed building.

Figure 5.3.2 *(right)*
The entrance hall.

Figure 5.3.3 *(bottom left)*
The ceiling of the design studio.

Credits

Building owner
Aston Martin Lagonda Limited

Architect
Weedon Partnership

Structural engineer
Techniker Ltd.

Engineer/Main contractor
Holzbau Saurer

5.3 Fast-track in timber: Aston Martin design studio, Gaydon, Warwickshire

The potential for timber frame to be a fast-track method of construction has been demonstrated for some forty years in the field of speculative house-building. The Aston Martin Studio *(Figure 5.3.1)*, however, is a large bespoke building for a prestige client, where timber was not the initial design solution.

The client, Aston Martin Lagonda Limited, required a new automotive design studio to be built within one year, otherwise a short-term temporary facility would be needed. The architects (the Weedon Partnership) prepared a design based on a steel frame, but when programmed it was found that this could not be constructed within the timescale. An alternative design based on timber was then developed in conjunction with the Austrian contractor Holzbau Saurer, which was time-compliant. The saving of the temporary facility was so dominant that no further cost comparisons were made. From first sketches, occupation was actually achieved within eleven months *(Figure 5.3.2)*.

The building has a plan area of some 2,700m² overall, and contains reception, showroom and support areas in two storeys, linked to a full-height design studio with a capacity of five full-sized clay models.

The foundations and ground floor are in concrete, with the entire super-structure in timber frame. The two-storey areas are framed convention-

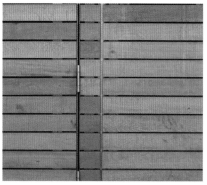

ally, with factory-made panels lined with plasterboard. The design studio is constructed with exposed glulam portals, which have mitred joints concealing steel flitch connecting plates with dowels *(Figures 5.3.3. 5.3.4)*. The north wall of the studio is entirely glazed, which allows the designers to assess the car models in natural light. To the south the two-storey structure offers viewing galleries at ground and first-floor levels. Externally, the building is clad with a rain-screen of horizontal oak boards, back-fixed and pre-assembled in panels, giving a precise and clean outline *(Figures 5.3.5. 5.3.6)*.

Despite the variations in the plan and structural form, the building frame took just four weeks to erect. The superstructure, walls and roof, and the whole building has been completed to the standards of design and construction which would be expected by such a client.

5.4 Supermarket frames in timber

For the last fifty years, the advice to designers in the UK wishing to over-roof a large area as economically as possible was to use a steel frame, as can be seen in supermarkets and do-it-yourself stores up and down the country. Recently, however, the global demand for steel, together with its manufacturing energy requirements, have led to significant price rises, while timber costs have not risen proportionately. In addition, there is now a regulatory need to assess the environmental impact of a building in quantitative terms, using for instance the methods given in BREEAM and the *Green guide to specification* which give timber a high rating.

Figure 5.3.4 *(top right)*
Detail of the portal joint. The main members are mitred, and then joined by two steel dowels, which can only just be seen. The 'aerofoil' purlin at high level supports the head of the full-height glazing panels.

Figure 5.3.5 *(left)*
Corner detail, showing the precision achieved with pre-fabricated components.

Figure 5.3.6 *(bottom right)*
Cladding detail; the boards are back-fixed, and their lines carried across a service door.

Figure 5.4.1 *(top right)*
General view of the interior.

Figure 5.4.2 *(top left)*
Typical bay of the roof structure, with diagonal bracing members.

Figure 5.4.3 *(middle left)*
Corner bays with tensioned rod bracing. Internal wall faces lined with birch ply.

Figure 5.4.4 *(bottom right)*
Line of rooflights.

Figure 5.4.5 *(bottom left)*
Signage boards.

For these reasons some supermarket chains have recently commissioned new stores which have timber frames, rather than steel. The first of these buildings, by Tesco, was opened in Wick, Scotland, in December 2006.

The frame essentially follows the standard supermarket structural form, with exposed glulam *(see Section 2.3.2)* posts on an 18 m x 12 m grid *(Figure 5.4.1)*. Beams are simply jointed over the posts by concealed steel flitch plates. Stability in the roof plane is achieved by glulam diagonals *(Figure 5.4.2)*,

and in the wall planes by crossed diagonal steel rods in selected bays *(Figure 5.4.3)*. Infill joists support a profiled metal deck laid to a shallow fall, with insulation and waterproofing over. Two lines of rooflights *(Figure 5.4.4)* provide increased illumination above the till areas. Services, principally lighting and ventilation trunking, are suspended from the roof, together with signage, neatly painted onto blockboard panels *(Figure 5.4.5)*.

External walls are also in timber, fabricated as full-height 6.7 m stressed skin panels, with I-beam webs and flanges of Kerto, and the 200 mm cavity filled with recycled newspaper. Internally the panels are lined with birch-faced ply *(Figure 5.4.3)*, and externally with ThermoWood® *(see Sections 2.3.7 and 5.3.1)* panels *(Figures 5.4.6, 5.4.7)*. The latter are, overall, weathering consistently, with only slight stain patterns around areas such as air vents.

To save road miles, since it is difficult to go further north than Wick, the frame components, and most of the other building materials, were transported to the site by ship.

The timber frame was just one of many 'green' initiatives which Tesco piloted at Wick. Others include:

- Reducing the standard internal height to minimise the heated space

- Roof-mounted wind turbines and solar cells

- Collection and re-use of rainwater

- Water-cooled refrigeration and cold air retrieval systems instead of air-conditioning units.

In all, at the time of writing, a dozen or so supermarkets are in progress or competed around the country, by Tesco and other chains.

Figure 5.4.6 *(left)*
ThermoWood® cladding to external walls.

Figure 5.4.7 *(right)*
Detail of horizontal shiplap boards.

Credits

Design
Ian Burke Associates

Engineer
Goodson Associates

Frame
Finnforest Merk

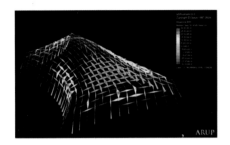

Figure 5.5.1
Sketch: Alvaro Siza

Figure 5.5.2
(above)

Figure 5.5.4
(below)

5.5 Computer conversations: Serpentine pavilion, Kensington Gardens, London. Summer 2005

The annual Serpentine Pavilions provide the opportunity for an architect who has not previously worked in the UK to build a landmark, albeit temporary building. The programme, which requires the building to be opened less than 20 weeks after the architect's initial sketch, always presents a particular challenge. The year 2005 marked the first of the pavilions to be conceived in timber and the first seamless use of computers from CAD to CAM, without ever touching paper – the only way that a building of such complex geometry could have been realised in such a short timescale.

The vision of the architects, Alvaro Siza and Eduardo Souto de Moura, was that of an insect waiting to pounce, with arched back and spread feet *(Figure 5.5.1)*. The structural consultants Arup suggested adapting the Lamella system *(see Section 4.1.4)*, invented by Zollinger in 1921, enabling the doubly curved organic form to be built up from a series of short straight elements, each with a central mortice and end tenons *(Figure 5.5.5)*. The

Figures 5.5.2–5.5.10
Photos and sketches: Arup

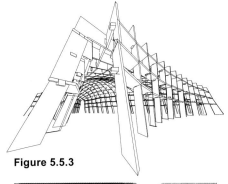

Figure 5.5.3

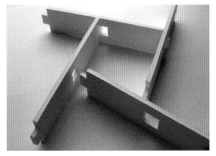

Figure 5.5.5

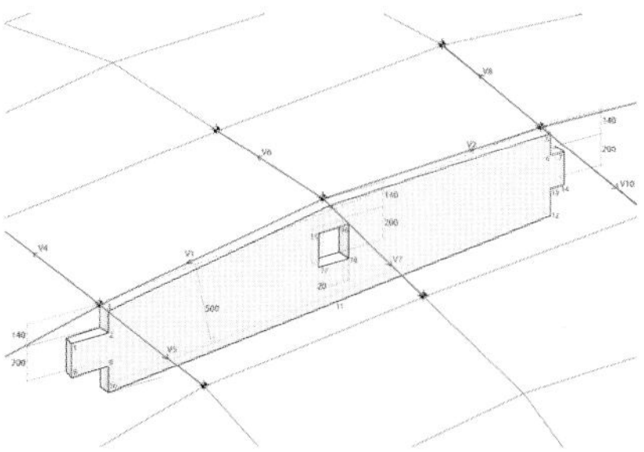

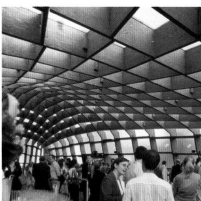

Figure 5.5.6

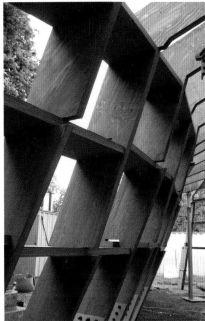

Figure 5.5.8

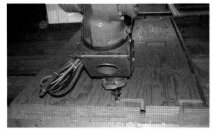

Figure 5.5.7

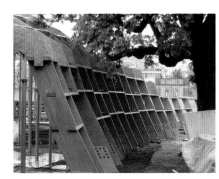

Figure 5.5.9

Figure 5.5.10

lamella was also carried down the walls and lent tremendous interest to the finished building, inviting the visitor to investigate how the 'jigsaw' had been assembled. The inside edges of the lamellas were cut square *(Figure 5.5.8)* to emphasise the short length of each piece, whereas the outside edges were cut to a warped profile *(Figure 5.5.9)*, creating the organic form and providing a smooth surface for the cladding.

The original lamellas were barrel vaults, in which every piece was identical. By contrast, to create the moulded form of the Pavilion each of the 427 pieces needed a unique geometry. It would have been quite possible to fill the entire programme simply by drawing every one of the different elements. The trick was a design which never touched the drawing board, but went straight from analytical model *(Figure 5.5.2)* to architectural rendering *(Figure 5.5.3)* and on to computer fabrication instructions. Instead of detailed drawings, Arup simply issued a spreadsheet defining the 36 coordinates of each element *(Figure 5.5.6)*. These were then used to drive the robotic arm at Finnforest Merk's factory just outside Munich. *Figure 5.5.7* shows the milling tool cutting one of the elements from a sheet of Kerto. *Figures 5.5.4 and 5.5.10* show the completed building.

Awards

Wood Awards 2005
Highly commended

Credits

Building owner
Serpentine Gallery

Architect
Alvaro Siza and Eduardo Souto de Moura

Engineer
Arup

Timber fabricator
Finnforest Merk

CASE STUDIES

Following the set of concise studies in chapter 5, showing examples of innovative uses of timber, the case studies in chapters 6 to 22 illustrate some of the key principles outlined in chapters 1 to 4.

Choosing only seventeen cases was an invidious task. They have been selected from an enormous range of recent work, and many other equally worthy examples could be presented, but space is limited. For more examples, readers should visit ww.trada.co.uk where TRADA continually showcases the best in timber architecture and engineering.

The studies are grouped as shown below and broadly follow, as far as this is practicable, the sequence in which major issues were covered in the preceding technical chapters.

6

Hodges Place, Offham, Kent

Peter Ross

Figure 6.01 *(previous page)*
View of the house, to the rear, with the extension and pool.

Hodges Place is a seventeenth century house on the outskirts of a village in Kent, with a steeply pitched catslide roof and tile hangings *(Figure 6.01)*. The owners wished to extend the property to provide for large family gatherings. The solution to this difficult problem was an extension in contrasting form – linear, open-plan, flat-roofed, and almost set apart from the original building, touching it only via a small entrance vestibule *(Figures 6.02, 6.03)*.

An old boundary wall was rebuilt to form the back wall of the extension, which looks out to the garden through a full-length window wall. The extension has a deliberately low profile; in fact it is let into the ground slightly and provided with a grass roof, irrigated in times of drought from the pool below, which is stocked with fish.

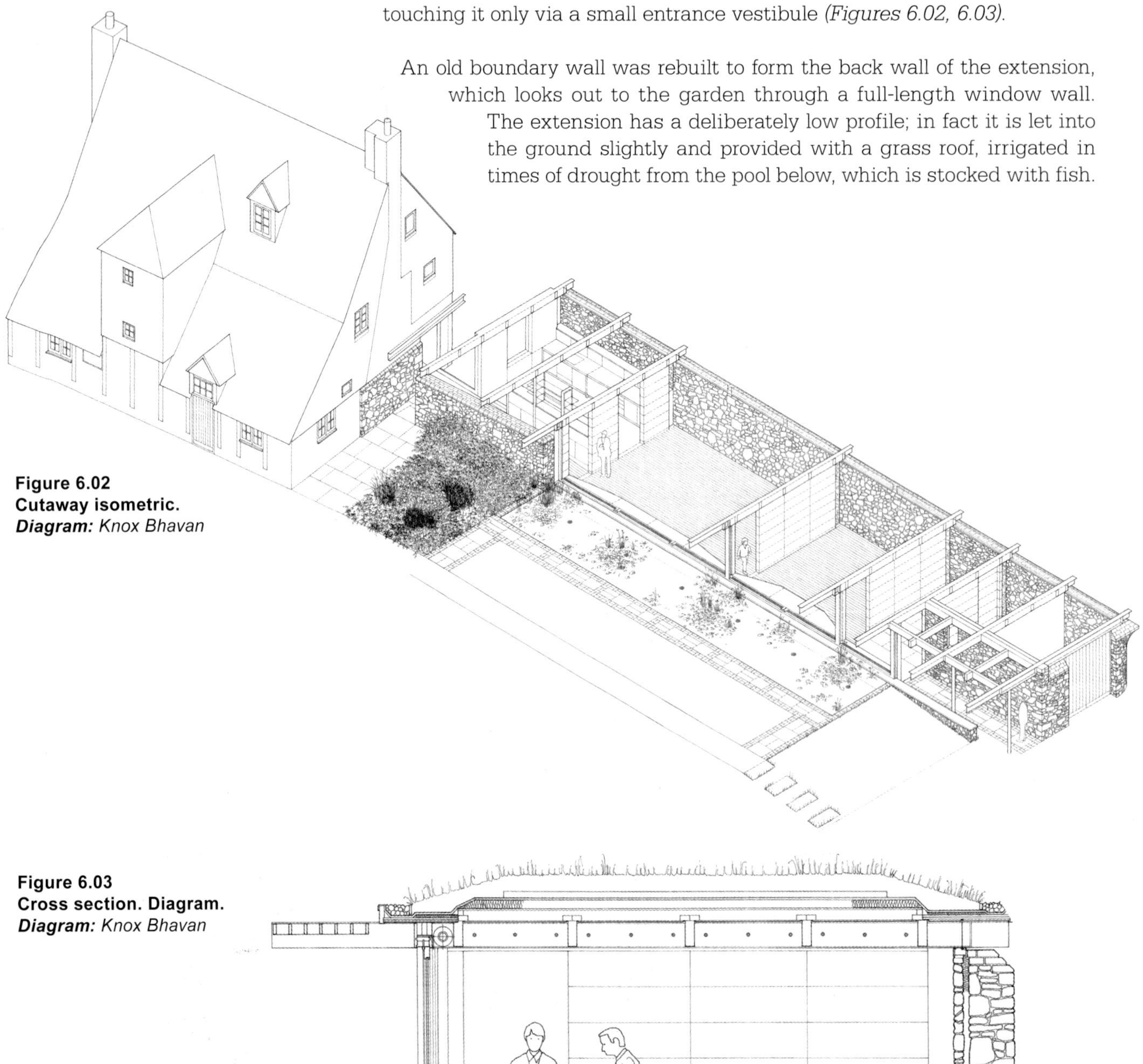

Figure 6.02
Cutaway isometric.
Diagram: Knox Bhavan

Figure 6.03
Cross section. Diagram.
Diagram: Knox Bhavan

The weight of the roof is taken by composite beams of steel I-joists, with Douglas fir planks bolted into the webs *(Figure 6.04)*. The secondary beams are in timber, infilled with ceiling panels of birch ply, sometimes animated with ripples of sunlight reflected from the pool.

Figure 6.04 *(left)*
View of the interior, with the roof supported by steel joists with Douglas fir infills to the webs. The joists span between the rear wall, and steel T-sections behind the window wall.

Room dividers are set along the extension, faced with cherry-wood veneer panels. Potentially awkward junctions between the dividers, the roof, and the rubble masonry wall are solved by the introduction of glass panels and narrow clerestory windows. To close off individual spaces, sliding glass doors are concealed within the dividers *(Figure 6.05)*. Continuity through the length is given by the window seat, with its undulating profile. The seat is close to pool water level, and with the windows open the effect is boat-like. The windows face due south, and are protected from the summer sun by a protecting brise-soleil in American white oak. The screen also has a second function: protecting the fish in the pond from the local herons who – say the owners – like to rise vertically after taking a catch.

Figure 6.05 *(above)*
A room divider, fitted with shelves on one side, and housing a sliding door.

While this extension receives some modest support from steel, its character is essentially determined by wood and stone linked through the glazed south elevation to water and the garden landscape beyond. Although a complete contrast to the original house, it is the perfect complement.

Awards

Wood Awards 2001
  Category: Private

Credits

Architect
  Knox Bhavan Architects

Structural engineer
  John Romer/Edward Cullinan

7

Carlisle Lane Lofts, London

Giles Downes

John Pringle and Penny Richards comprise two thirds of the architectural practice Pringle Richard Sharratt. When their two university-aged children needed accommodation, they therefore decided to use their capital and expertise to build new apartments for the children rather than simply finding them flats.

Their site was an old single-storey warehouse next to where the Waterloo Necropolis Station used to be, by a railway viaduct on the South Bank to the south of Westminster Bridge Road. After extensive negotiations with the planners, consent was granted for four flats on two storeys, two at 35 m² and two at 45 m², with a narrow courtyard down one side providing the entrance, staircases and shared garden space *(Figure 7.01)*.

The architects had previous experience of using engineered timber (see Section 2.3.5), and were keen to develop the range of what could be achieved with this material.

Working with specialist contractor Eurban, they developed the design using prefabricated panels of solid timber made by Finnforest Merk in Germany. These panels are laminated up from layers of Spruce softwood, each layer alternately cross-laminated into solid stable panels which are load-bearing

Figure 7.01 *(opposite page)*
The courtyard at night.
Photo: Edmund Sumner / VIEW

Figure 7.02 *(right)*
Ground floor and first floor plans.
Diagram: Pringle Richards Sharratt

Figure 7.03 *(below)*
Axonometric view of building.
Diagram: Pringle Richards Sharratt

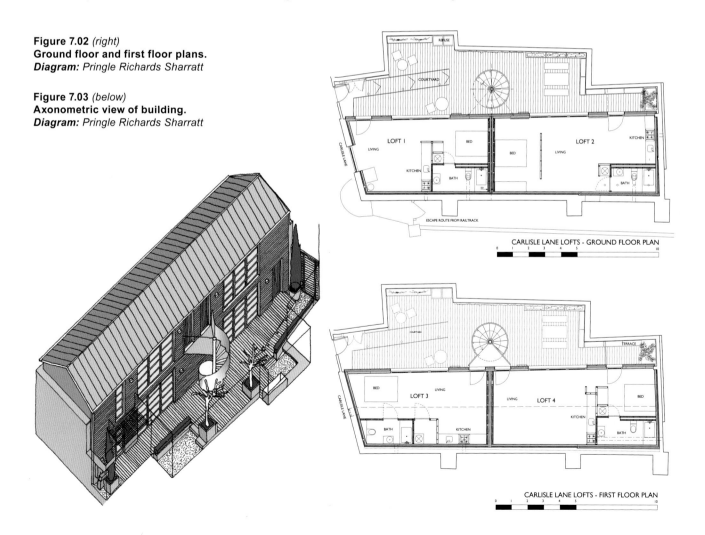

CARLISLE LANE LOFTS - GROUND FLOOR PLAN

CARLISLE LANE LOFTS - FIRST FLOOR PLAN

Figure 7.04
Panels being assembled.
Photo: Eurban

Awards

Wood Awards 2005
Highly commended

The judges commented that this was 'an interesting, well executed project that will provide very comfortable first homes. The system uses a lot of wood but with current acoustic regulations this is a good way of complying'.

Credits

Client
Pringle and Richard

Architect
Pringle Richard Sharrat

Structural engineer
Alan Baxter and Associates

Main contractor
Eurban

Joinery
Finnforest Merk

and structural, and can form walls, floors and roof to make a complete light-weight building. In this case, the light weight was particularly important as it avoided the need for new foundations on what was old marshy filled ground under the warehouse.

The panels are cut to size and shape with computer-controlled routers (CNC), and window openings and routes for service runs can all be cut accurately in the factory. The whole building can then be flat-packed and delivered to site for very fast and straightforward erection.

The solid timber panels for the apartments were erected close against the old brick walls of the warehouse, which were also the boundary walls of the site *(Figure 7.02)*. The gaps were filled with insulation and the inner timber panels formed an independent load-bearing wall to avoid complications with party wall agreements. The outer brick walls also provided weather-proofing and fire resistance.

Other open side facing towards the garden *(Figure 7.03)* is constructed of solid panels clad with wood fibre insulation with an outer rain screen of Thermowood boarding. This is heat-treated spruce which has been taken to 200 degrees centigrade during the curing process, which makes the timber stable and weather resistant.

The laminated panels can absorb moisture and as long as the insulation is more vapour permeable than the panels, then it is not necessary to install a vapour barrier. This allows the building to breath naturally and for water vapour to escape without special ventilation.

In fact the permeability for vapour and the thermal inertia of the solid timber panels provide significantly better sustainability than the alternative option of SIPs (structural insulated panels made up of two layers of board bonded together with Urethane foam insulation). The greater weight of the solid timber panels is more than offset by the advantages above.

The laminated panels are joined with compressible rubber seals at wall and floor junctions to make airtight joints.

During construction *(Figure 7.04)* the most noticeable effect of using this system is the simple direct erection of the roof, where the panels form each pitch with no requirement for inner cross-framing or bracing.

In order to achieve the sound insulation that is required in modern dwellings, the party walls were made with two independent panel walls side by side, and the party floors were made up with plaster board ceilings on resilient hangers below, and fibre board and insulation making up the floor construction above.

These solid timber panels are growing in popularity. They can form the load-bearing and structural elements of a building very quickly and effectively to provide fully sustainable and very fast construction on site.

The project has been very successful, providing four comfortable studio apartments for the client.

8

CASE STUDY

Haberdashers' Hall

Giles Downes

Figure 8.03 *(previous page)*
First floor reception gallery.
Photo: Peter Mackinven/VIEW

Figure 8.01
Ground floor (a) and first floor (b) plans.
Drawing: Michael Hopkins & Partners

1 Entrance hall
2 Porter's lodge
3 Loggia
4 Courtyard
5 Colonnade
6 Orangery
7 Main stair
8 Cloaks
9 Members' facilities
10 Offices
11 Kitchen
12 Staff area
13 Loading bay
14 Refuse
15 Service yard

1 Livery hall
2 Reception gallery
3 Luncheon room
4 Court room
5 Committee room
6 Main stair
7 Display room
8 Drawing room
9 Library
10 Master's flat
11 Beadle's flat
12 Clerk's flat
13 Servery
14 Wine bin

Like most Ancient Livery companies the Worshipful Company of Haberdashers have occupied several Halls since the granting of their first Royal Charter in 1448. As each has been catastrophically destroyed, a new one has been built, the second Hall after the Great Fire of London and its successor after the Second World War.

The third Hall, which was completed in 1956, was considered to be undistinguished and outdated for the use of the company. The old site was therefore

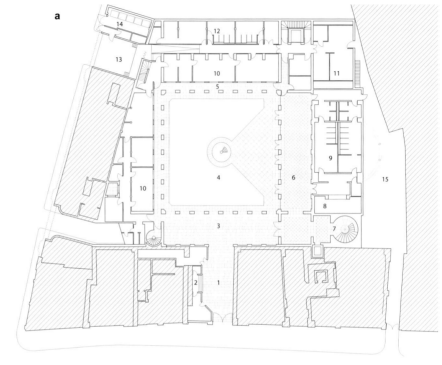

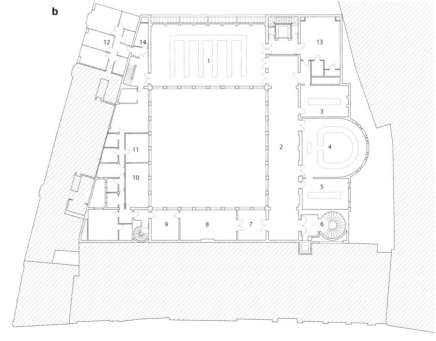

sold in 1996 for commercial redevelopment, revitalising the finances of the Company and allowing them to build a fourth Hall on a new site in Smithfield to see them into the 21st Century. The new site was set behind existing buildings facing onto West Smithfield with only a narrow frontage between existing buildings, and the Company chose Michael Hopkins and Partners as their architects.

Hopkins reorganised the site with the new buildings ranged around the private central courtyard on two storeys *(Figure 8.01)*. An arched entrance with a porter's lodge and gates provides a glimpse into this court from the street.

The new courtyard is given the calm classical feel of an Oxford college through the use of simple regular brick elevations with a colonnaded cloister on the ground floor and matching large window openings above *(Figure 8.02)*.

The entrance sequence subtly modifies the regularity of this arrangement, starting with the porch and entrance passage leading to the first open colonnade on the eastern side. From here glass doors lead into the enclosed glazed cloister on the northern side, which acts as a ground floor reception area with cloak rooms and WCs behind.

The west and south sides of the ground floor are occupied by offices, kitchens and service areas, faced with timber behind a narrow open cloister providing a covered passageway on these sides.

From the northeast corner of the ground floor reception area, a large spiral staircase leads up to the formal rooms above. Up to this point the main finishes have been brick, precast concrete and stone, but on the first floor the formal spaces of the Hall are more richly finished with American white oak paneling *(Figures 8.03, 8.04)*. This species was chosen for its calm straight grain, availability, and continuity of characteristics, to allow an even finish throughout the large quantities required for the Hall.

Figure 8.02 *(above)*
View from courtyard looking North.
Photo: *American Hardwood Export Council*

Figure 8.04 *(left)*
Livery Hall on first floor.
Photo: *American Hardwood Export Council*

Credits

Client
The Worshipful Company of
Haberdashers

Architect
Michael Hopkins & Partners

Structural & services engineer
Arup

Main contractor
Holloway White Allom

The appearance of this timber reflects the simplicity and clarity of the entire design, in which all the architectural elements are expressed, but with the greatest restraint, held to the surface like a subtle calligraphy on the walls and ceilings of the formal rooms.

This effect is clearest in the expression of the roof structure to the Livery Hall *(Figure 8.04)*, which continues the theme of a diagonal structural grid that is also explored in other projects by Hopkins and Partners, such as Portcullis House *(see Case Study 12)*.

The Hall is 20 m x 10 m in plan with a 45 degree pitched hipped roof. The structure of this roof is made up of 400 mm x 100 mm glue-laminated beams, the bottom lamination being American white oak. Each length of beam is trimmed and slotted into a flush U-shaped stainless steel shoe at both ends. These are then bolted to stainless steel nodes to connect them together into a structural diagonal grid forming each face of the hipped roof.

To brace the roof, stainless steel rods are connected with tension ties to the stainless steel shoes at the feet of the grid, where the latter sits on concrete pre-cast padstones expressed and set flush into the inner wall lining. These tie rods are in turn connected with 60 mm diameter props, to make up a tensioned lattice inside the roof space.

Set within the depth of the diagrid are 50 mm x 175 mm rafters, which brace the structure and hold 18 mm plywood infill panels and insulation.

The outer face of the roof is finished with prefabricated panels made up of lead sheeting over plywood squares set in a diamond pattern to reflect the diagrid structure *(Figure 8.02)*. These are fixed with battens over a breather membrane on an 18 mm plywood outer deck, leaving a 50 mm ventilated cavity.

The inner faces of the Hall roof are clad with American white oak slats made up into diamond-shaped acoustic panels. These are set into the diagrid, flush with the lower face with 10 mm shadow gaps (which are used throughout the design). Behind the slatted face Hessian-covered acoustic quilts provide sound absorption. At the apex of the roof open slatted panels provide ventilation though to upper roof vents.

The roof over the first floor reception area is a smaller and simpler version of the same design, faced internally with solid white oak infill panels.

The walls and floor are also finished in American white oak panelling and boarding over insulation and service plenums.

The new Hall around its cloistered courtyard gives a great sense of serenity and timelessness. The Livery Hall is like a beautifully finished box to make a suitable housing for the formal dinners and banquets that it accommodates.

The building overall is well liked by the Haberdashers Company and has been very successful. The elegance and austerity of its architecture provide an object lesson in clearly thought through design and attention to detail. It was highly commended in the Wood Awards.

9

CASE STUDY

Norwich Cathedral:
Visitor Centre

Giles Downes

Figure 9.01 *(previous page)*
Outside view of visitor centre.
Photo: Paul Tyagi / VIEW

Norwich Cathedral is one of the finest Norman buildings in Europe, and the Dean and Chapter of the Cathedral needed a new visitors' centre that would cater for the thousands of visitors without affecting the marvellous historic and religious interiors.

After years of negotiation with heritage conservation bodies, permission for the new building was given and a grant was obtained from the Heritage Lottery Fund. This, together with other charitable donations, made sufficient funds available for the first phase of the project to proceed. This takes the form of a new restaurant on the site of the original medieval refectory outside the cloister to the Cathedral.

Michael Hopkins and Partners were selected as architects, and the main requirement for their design was that the new building should be clearly modern in contrast to the original fabric, but should at the same time be sympathetic and enhance the quality of the medieval building.

The new visitor centre, which was finished in 2004, sits lightly in the space between the ruined outer wall of the refectory and the inner wall to the library over the cloister itself. These old stone walls were carefully and discreetly restored to form the boundaries to the new space *(Figure 9.01)*, and the outer wall was brought to a consistent level parallel with the base of the old external windows to the library opposite.

Figure 9.02
A gently tapered column of honey-coloured oak, capped with a stainless steel connector from which four oak struts radiate out to support the roof.
Photo: Buro Happold

The new restaurant occupies an upper mezzanine timber deck at this level, looking out over the outer wall and sitting over the top of a timber-faced box that houses the kitchens, services, and WCs. The spaces that have been carefully left between this new box and the medieval walls provide access corridors on both sides..

The outer edges of the box rise up as glass balustrades to the restaurant floor, fitting between nine pairs of slender turned oak laminated columns, which support the oversailing roof and are braced by the box.

The columns are gently tapered and capped with special stainless steel connectors. From the head of each of these columns, four turned oak struts radiate out to support the roof like an umbrella *(Figure 9.02)* so that no horizontal frames or ties are needed. The stainless steel strut connectors were specially developed for this project by Buro Happold in order to carry the weight of the roof, and at the same time allow for movements in the frame structure, so that all the members could be kept as slim and light as possible.

The roof itself is made up of parallel pitched frames with insulation infill, faced on the inside with flush oak boarding and slotted oak panels to provide sound absorption. On the inner edge of the roof a continuous row of double-glazed openable roof lights provide daylight to the library windows below. The outer edge of the roof rests over a clerestory of opening wiindows shaded by sawn oak louvered panels with wide horizontal oak slats sitting on top of the outer medieval wall.

The roof is clad in traditional lead with ridge ventilation and large lead-lined steel framed gutters, forming a strong outer edge to the roof on one side and a floating link to the old library wall on the other.

Figure 9.03
Entrance to the restaurant, with freestanding glazed lift and glass and steel stair.
Photo: Paul Tyagi / VIEW

Awards

Wood Awards 2004
Gold award

Commercial and Public Access award

RIBA Award 2005

Structural Heritage Award 2005
The Institution of Structural Engineers

Credits

Client
The Dean and Chapter, Norwich Cathedral

Architect
Michael Hopkins & Partners

Structural engineer
Buro Happold

Main contractor
RG Carter, Norfolk

The inner service box and restaurant deck stop one bay short at the ends of the building, and are closed with full height glazing so that the roof sails out over a three-storey open volume at each end, supported on the last pair of slender full-height columns. In these spaces, the architects have placed the vertical circulation and the entrance to the restaurant with a freestanding glazed lift and glass and steel stairs at each end *(Figure 9.03)*.

The internal finishes are dominated by the soft honey colour of light oak set against the old stone walls and fine elements of stainless steel and light grey painted steel framing.

The initial effect on visiting the building is the rough outer stone wall facing the car park, with the sawn oak louvre panels and the lead-finished roof marrying in well with the medieval fabric of the Cathedral. It is when looking into the full-height glazed ends that the form of the new building and its relationship to the old is immediately apparent. The drama of the lift and stairs moving through these spaces adds life and movement to the architecture.

The contrast of the light, modern materials of the new building, set against the texture and weight of the medieval, brings out the best of each and enhances both. The simplicity of the design approach belies its subtlety and effectiveness so that the experience of moving through and using the building is an over-whelming one of space and light, with the warm colour of the smooth wood surfaces and the texture of the old stone making one harmonious whole.

The building is a delight to visit and has been a great success with the thousands of visitors to the Cathedral.

10

The Savill Building, Windsor
Giles Downes

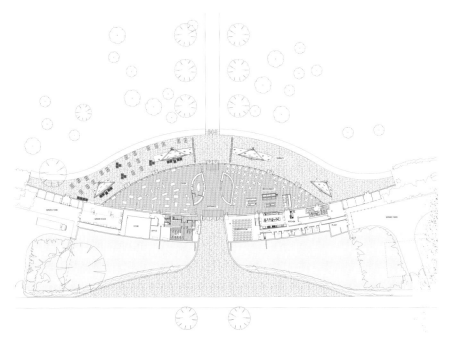

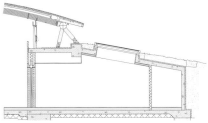

Figure 10.03 (opposite page)
The underside of the roof seen from the garden.
Photo: Giles Downes

Figure 10.01
Plan and section.
Drawing: Glenn Howells Architects

Figure 10.02 (below left)
View from rear.
Photo: Giles Downes

The Crown Estates needed a new visitor centre for their established woodland Savill Gardens, which were first started in the 1930s in Windsor Great Park.

From a short list of three architects, they selected Glenn Howells on the basis of his proposal for a lightweight sustainable building that would make the most of the dramatic landscape setting and use local renewable materials from the Crown Estate forest.

Figure 10.04 (above)
The interior.
Photo: Giles Downes

The Savill Gardens are entered by road at the top of a rise where there is space for car parking, and from which the gardens themselves fall away into a sheltered valley. The plan *(Figure 10.01)* shows how the architects were able to arrange all the service and support areas, kitchens and offices on the entrance side under a shallow rising green roof sloping up as a bank from the car park. Beyond this they could then house the open reception area, shop and restaurant under a single elegant timber gridshell, leaf shaped in plan, and based on the concept first used by Edward Cullinan Architects at the Weald and Downland Museum in Sussex – *see Case Study 11*.

The gridshell (*see section 4.1.5*) takes the double curved 'peanut' form that has become familiar from the Weald and Downland Museum (*Figures 10.02-04*), but at 90 metres long it is four times the size of its predecessor, and is arranged as a large central vault flanked by two smaller ones on either side.

The Savill gridshell also differs from the Weald and Downland design by being lifted up and supported on a steel ring beam so that it can be open sided and, positioned along the edge of the ridge, afford panoramic views out over the landscape and gardens beyond. From the entrance parking area the shell is therefore raised to float above the bank formed by the green roofed service areas, over a clerestory of opening windows which provide light and cross-ventilation to the main central area.

The edge ring beam is formed of tubular steel, curved to follow the undulations of the shell (*Figure 10.05*). The use of this ring beam affects the structure of the shell by reducing the degree to which the timbers need to be bent. This eases the initial construction process, but requires the shell stiffness to be increased to deal with the shallower forms.

The Green Oak Carpentry Company and Buro Happold Structural Engineers were able to build on the experience they gained in constructing the Weald and Downland Museum. The shell is constructed of four layers of 80 x 50 mm

Figure 10.05 (above)
The rear terrace.
Photo: Giles Downes

Figure 10.06 (right)
The exposed structure of larch laths before being covered with plywood, a layer of insulation, a standing seam waterproof roof, and finally a rain screen of English oak slats.
Photo: Warwick Sweeney/The Royal Landscape

Figure 10.07
The finger-jointing of the laths.
Photo: Warwick Sweeney/The Royal Landscape

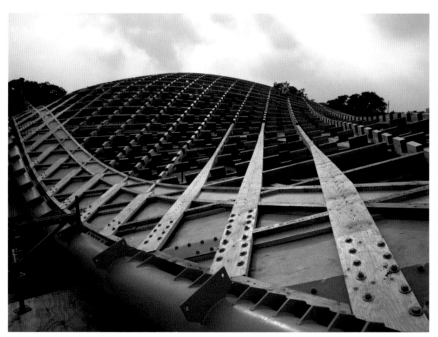

larch laths (*Figure 10.06*), with spacing blocks to provide a deeper stiffer structural shell where required. The two inner layers were assembled flat on a temporary scaffold platform, bolted together, and then lifted into the double-curved form. The intermediate spacer blocks were fitted over these, and the outer two layers were attached to complete the shell (*see Section 4.1.5*).

Birch plywood was fitted over the shell, with sheathing and insulation and a standing seam waterproof roof. The exterior of the roof is clad with a rain screen of English oak slats, which extends well beyond the edge ring beam to give a brise-soleil overhang which shades the restaurant terrace.

The undulating curved form gives rise to some areas of higher load concentration, particularly at the edges of the shells. In the Weald and Downland gridshell this was dealt with through additional laths, but at Savill Gardens the loads had to be transferred to the steel edge beam. To deal with the concentration of these loads Kerto® *(see section 2.3.3)* was used as a strong stable transitional material between the steel beam and the grid of larch laths *(Figure 10.06)*.

Sustainability was essential to the entire design concept. Glenn Howells wanted a building that 'intelligently used sustainable resources to inform the design and create an integrated solution to environmental control, structure and light'.

The oak for the roof rain screen and for the main floor was harvested from the Crown Estate Forests, as were the larch wood laths for the structural shell. These larch trees had been close-planted in the 1930s by the Crown Estate woodsman and high pruned in the 1950s to produce long clear stems. Mature stems over 70 years old are now felled and replaced on a continuous basis to Forest Stewardship Council criteria. Some 400 trees were harvested to provide the laths for this project, which were finger-jointed together to make up the long lengths required. This finger-jointing *(Figure 10.07)* also allowed an efficient high yield of over 50% good quality sawn timber from the round log.

The main areas of the building are naturally ventilated with mechanical ventilation limited to the service support areas of the kitchens, WCs and lecture room.

Lifting the gridshell has allowed large areas of panoramic glazing using low E glass panels set in timber frames. This provides good natural lighting shaded by deep roof overhangs of up to 4.5 m to reduce glare and solar gain. The gridshell and the green roofs throughout are highly insulated and the building is fitted with underfloor heating and high efficiency boilers.

The organization of the plan and the form and siting of the building have provided an exciting and elegant new visitors centre which gives an overriding effect of light and space, carrying through high quality design and workmanship at every level.

The building is very enjoyable to visit and has been highly successful. Jay Merrick, architectural correspondent for the Independent, commented that 'this project has lifted the gridshell into the mainstream of architectural practice in Britain'.

Awards

Wood Awards 2006
  Gold award

Supreme Award for Structural Engeneering Excellence 2007
  The Institution of Structural Engineers

RIBA award 2007

Rural Design Award 2007
  for a timber building from the Civic Trust

Credits

Client
  Crown Estates

Architect
  Glenn Howells Architects

Timber Structure Engineer
  Buro Happold

Roof Design Consultant and Contractor
  The Green Oak Carpentry Company

Structural Engineer
  HRW

Services Engineer
  Atelier 10

Main Contractor
  William Verry

CASE STUDY

Weald and Downland
Open Air Museum

11

Giles Downes

The Weald & Downland Open Air Museum, near Chichester in Sussex, needed a new building to house their collection of old tools and artefacts and to provide a much needed conservation workshop and teaching space. At the same time they wanted a worthy modern addition to their collection of 13th to 19th century buildings that would be an inspiration for visitors and would show what can now be achieved in timber. In a collaboration between Edward Cullinan Architects and the engineers Buro Happold, the new building was designed to answer that brief and was completed in 2003.

The building is sited on a steeply sloping wooded hillside in the museum grounds, close to the entrance ticket office and shop. The hillside is terraced to provide visitors' car parking under the trees, and the new building takes advantage of this to house the collection within a semi-basement set into the hillside on a lower terrace. This lower floor in reinforced concrete and blockwork provides the exhibition and the support and service areas within a strong stable base, on which the lightweight timber gridshell can sit to form the upper-storey open workshop space *(Figure 11.01)*.

This was the first use of a gridshell structure *(see Section 4.1.5)* in a major building in the UK. The gridshell is made up of a diagonal lattice of several layers of long timber battens, curved to form a shell vault. The shell is based on a catenary arch form and is doubly curved into a series of interconnected vaults, with intervening saddle forms (rather like a peanut) *(Figure 11.02)* in order to give stability and to cover as much space as possible. It is made up of four layers of thin 50 x 35 mm oak laths, which have been finger-jointed together to make up the 36 m lengths that are required to span diagonally over the internal space. The laths are taken down to floor level where they are fixed back to the stable base formed by the floor over the semi-basement.

These laths were first laid up together as a flat diagonal grid on a 7m high temporary scaffold, and were held together at their node crossing points by specially designed bolted clamp connectors *(Chapter 4, Figure 4.38)*. The purpose of the connectors was to allow the positions of the crossing points to be adjusted as the scaffold was lowered and the diagonal grid was slowly bent down into shape. They also avoided the weakening of the laths at their maximum stress positions that would have been caused by using drill fixings at the crossing points.

Once the grid had assumed its final shape and the laths had been fixed back to the floor, the internal scaffold was removed *(Figures 11.04, 11.05)*. The outside of the shell was then covered with reflective membrane roof

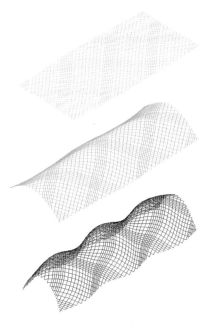

Figure 11.04 *(above)*
The building in progress.
Photo: Mandy Reynolds

Figure 11.06 *(bottom right)*
The rib shell being constructed.
Photo: Buro Happold/Adam Wilson

Figure 11.07 *(top middle)*
The armadillo-like layers of overlapping cladding, and above them the sloping translucent rooflight.
Photo: Giles Downes

Figure 11.08 *(top right)*
The building at night.
Photo: Buro Happold/Adam Wilson

sheathing and insulation, with an outer cladding of homegrown western red cedar *(Figure 11.07)*.

Edward Cullinan designed the building using physical modeling, and Buro Happold carried out advance computer analysis to achieve the best shape for the internal space and a stable structure to withstand wind and snow loads *(Figure 11.03)*.

The loads on the structural grid vary at different points along the form, and this has been dealt with by halving the centres between laths and so doubling the framing. This concentration of laths emphasises the shape and the flowing curves of the structural grid internally, giving a marvellous sinuous linear quality to the form.

Along the centre line of the gridshell an outer roof is formed as a sinuous ribbon of upper capping between vertical clerestory opening windows on both sides. This is flanked on both sides by sloping insulated translucent roof lights which form the uppermost of four tiers of external cladding, over-lapped in stages like the shell of an armadillo *(Figure 11.07)*. Each tier slopes

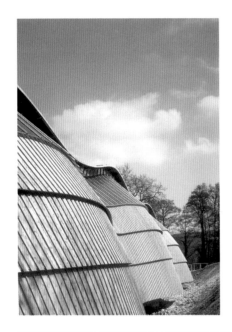

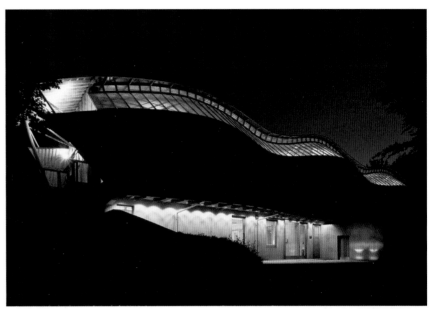

down more towards the first floor base following the curving arched shape of the gridshell. The three lower tiers are made up of lapped cedar boards alternately inner and outer, which have now weathered to a gentle silver grey colour.

The final roof profile is complex and the radii, even for green oak, are very tight. Both of these factors slowed down the process of bending the gridshell into its final shape *(see Section 4.1.5)*. Some materials such as the oak laths could not be sourced locally, and in the end French oak was used. A benefit of this whole process has been the generation of an enthusiastic partnership of hands-on expertise. This has since led to the establishment of the Timberbuild Network in the UK, which is intended to re-establish links between woodland producers and the construction industry.

The materials for the gridshell are sustainable timber including oak for the structural grid, home-grown Western red cedar for the cladding, British spruce for the floor plate, and English ash for the workshop floor. Scandinavian spruce and Siberian larch have been used for the glulam posts, beams and arches, which set the form and provide the entrances at each end of the building.

The whole building has a presence which fits extremely well into its surroundings, almost like an animal in its wooded sloping setting, and gives a huge volume of space with minimal impact on the landscape. Internally, it provides a delightful and exciting open space some 46 m long and up to 9 m high.

Although it is an experimental structure, this gridshell building has been hugely successful and is very popular with visitors. It was runner-up for the Stirling Prize as well as receiving the awards listed here. It has led to a new generation of similar structures and is a most worthy addition to the Weald and Downland Open Air Museum's collection of timber buildings. It is certainly a most inspiring building to visit and provides a very successful working space for the museum conservation workshops and a teaching space for seminars.

12

Portcullis House, Westminster, London

Peter Ross

Figure 12.03 *(previous page)*
Structural members of paired glulams forming a diagonal grid. The photograph shows the high degree of transparency achieved by this solution.

Since the 1980s, studies of the Palace of Westminster have consistently shown the need for more parliamentary office space and meeting rooms. The opportunity came when the site on the corner of Westminster Bridge Road and the Victoria Embankment was cleared for the construction of the Jubilee Line underground station *(Figure 12.01)*. This opened up the possibility at ground level of a new free-standing building which could nevertheless be linked by a subway to the Palace. The building, designed by Michael Hopkins and Partners, takes the form of a hollow rectangle, with a courtyard at ground level covered by a glazed roof, providing a circulation hub and meeting place. The station works in the ground imposed severe constraints on the superstructure. The entire load on the courtyard wall had to be taken on six columns, located in the only positions which would allow direct transmission of the building load to the foundation *(Figure 12.02)*.

Figure 12.01
The relationship between the supporting columns and the London Underground lines.
***Drawing:** Michael Hopkins and Partners*

1 Courtyard
2 District & Circle lines
3 Escalator box
4 Eastbound Jubilee line
5 Westbound Jubilee line

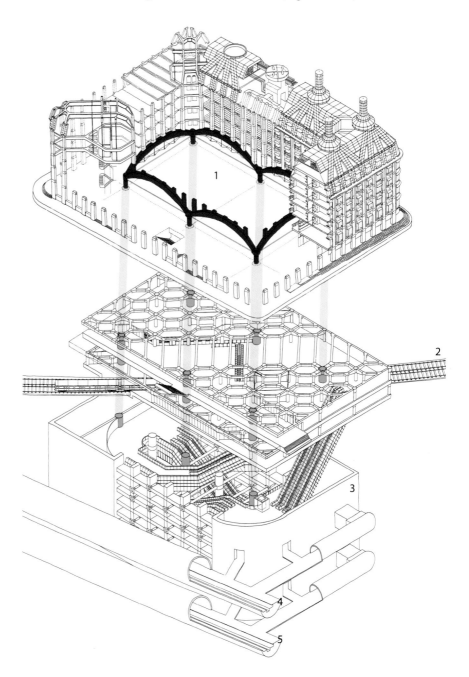

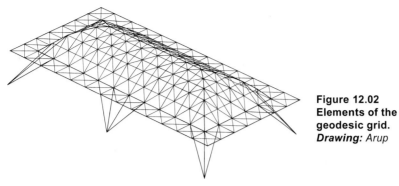

Figure 12.02
Elements of the
geodesic grid.
Drawing: Arup

Figure 12.04
Corner node, supported on a 'cigar'
column.

Figure 12.05
The subsidiary grid in metal,
supporting the glazing panels.

The courtyard roof takes the form of a glazed barrel vault, with hipped ends and a perimeter flat for maintenance access, supported by a geodesic frame in timber frame with raking struts which bring the load down to the six columns *(Figure 12.03)*. The aim was to create a very light structure with no bracing system below the main frame (to maximise the transparency of the roof) and, if possible, fabricated from American white oak only 200 mm in depth.

The structural engineers for the project, Arup, made a preliminary analysis of the frame which, in the central area, acts predominantly as an arch. Loads due to self-weight would be largely compressive, but asymmetric loads, such as drifted snow, would produce significant bending stresses. Members which were only 200 mm deep would have a span-to-depth ratio of 110 – over twice the default value given in *Section 4.1.2*. The analysis showed that the stresses were high, but that timber of class D50 would be sufficient – see *Section 2.3.1*. This is a very high strength for temperate hardwoods (European oak could only be rated at D40) and there was little information available on the structural use of American white oak, as it is more normally used for joinery. However, tests on 'small clears' *(see Section 2.1.1)* showed that it was stronger than European oak, and that material was generally available that was straight-grained, with few knots.

Arup commissioned BRE to undertake a programme of testing, which showed that timber drawn from stock of 'First and second' quality, could qualify as D50 grade. Thus the members were fabricated from paired glulams, each 100 mm x 200 mm deep *(Figure 12.05)*.

The frame joints were conceived in principle as metal components, with flitch plates between the paired timbers joined to a central node. The nodes would have to transmit compression (and in places tension), shear, and bending forces. There are in all many different joint arrangements, and so the design was rationalised by setting a solid steel sphere at the node point, with standard blades profiled to fit the sphere simply welded on at the appropriate angles *(Figure 12.04)* and *(Chapter 3, Figure 3.09d)*. The raking struts, or 'cigar' columns, were turned from 300 mm square blocks of glulam oak, and the glazing panels, half the size of the structural grid, are supported on a subsidiary infill grid of tensioned metal rods *(Figure 12.05)*. Motorised ventilation panels are concealed behind the 'lights', which are in fact simply reflectors, avoiding the problem of access at height.

Following the BRE testing work on the white oak, the American Hardwood Export Council (AHEC) commissioned tests on three further species with potential structural use, and published the results. For further information contact the AHEC at www.ahec.org.

Credits

Client
The Parliamentary Works
Directorate

Architect
Michael Hopkins and Partners

Structural engineer
Arup

Construction Manager
Laing Management Ltd

Kingsdale School, London

Giles Downes

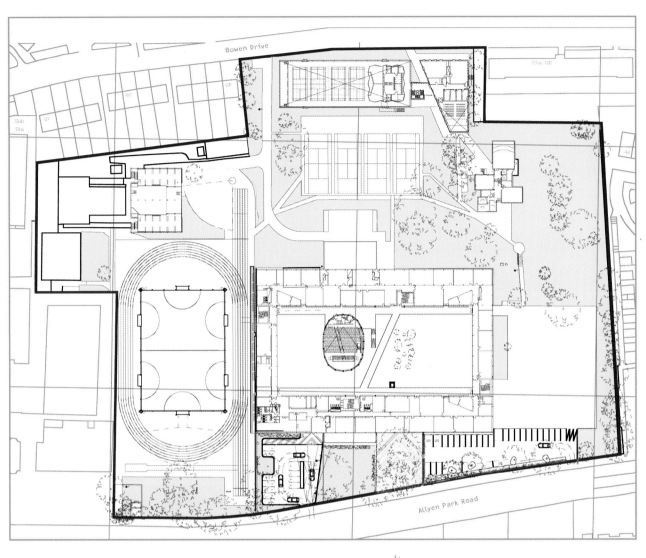

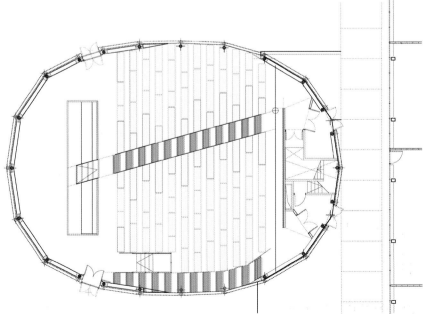

Figure 13.01
Site plan, showing new
central roofed space
containing timber egg.
Drawing: dRMM

Figure 13.02
Ground floor plan.
Drawing: dRMM

Figure 13.09 *(opposite page)*
Auditorium interior.
Photo: Michael Mack

Kingsdale School was designed in the 1950s by Leslie Martin of the LCC, as a system-built school for the future arranged around central open courtyards on a one hectare site. It is next to Dulwich College Preparatory School in south east London.

After 50 years, the building was tired and out of date and it was recognised as a failing school with poor attendance and academic results. A bold £10 million initiative was undertaken jointly by the Architecture Foundation/Schoolworks and the Department for Education and Skills, to determine whether a radical renovation and architectural rethinking of the old buildings could improve the environment sufficiently to turn the failing school around and raise standards.

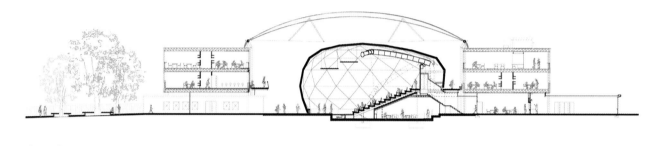

0   5m

Figure 13.03
Longitudinal section through hall and ovoid auditorium.
Drawing: dRMM

De Rijke Marsh Morgan (dRMM) were selected as architects, and together with the environmental engineers Fulcrum and the structural engineers Michael Hadi Associates, a dramatic scheme was developed to open the central courtyards into a single space covered with an adjustable lightweight roof of transparent plastic envelopes *(Figures 13.01-13.03)*. This roof and a new timber-framed auditorium were completed in 2004.

This roof to the great central space is similar to the domes at the Eden Project in Cornwall, and consists of a series of large sealed cushions made of layers of ETFE (Ethylene tetrafluoroethylene, a transparent plastic with high strength and corrosion resistance) held in a lightweight framework and kept continuously inflated by a small supply of air under pressure *(Figures 13.04, 13.05)*. The resulting roof is rigid and strong while remaining very light in weight and providing good insulation from the trapped air in the cushions.

Figure 13.04
New central court with lightweight roof over 'wooden egg' style auditorium.
Photo: Alex de Rijke

Figure 13.05
Node in geodesic structure of auditorium roof.
Photo: *Alex de Rijke*

Figure 13.06
Auditorium in central court.
Photo: *Alex de Rijke*

Figure 13.07
Auditorium in central court.
Photos: Alex de Rijke

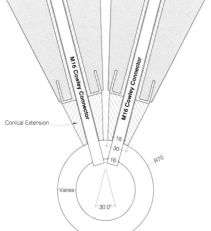

Figure 13.08a
Detail of the Cowley connector.
Drawing: Cowley Timberwork

Figure 13.08b
Detail of the Cowley connector.
Photo: Cowley Timberwork

By introducing a central third layer of ETFE, each cushion is then divided into two layers so that any heat loss via internal convection through the trapped air is further reduced. This subdivision at the same time offers a very elegant solution to solar gain, which would otherwise become a serious issue in the enclosed space below. To achieve this, a light-reflective coating is applied in a pattern to the inner face of the outer layer of the cushion, and in an alternate pattern to the middle layer of ETFE. As the outer and inner cushions can be kept inflated by separate air supplies, it is possible through the control of these to deflate the upper cushions and inflate the lower, thus pushing the middle layer upwards. This makes the alternate reflective patterns on the two layers join together as a continuous reflective surface to cut off sunlight. Alternatively, by inflating the upper and deflating the lower cushions the reflective patterns can be pushed apart thus allowing in more sunlight. By use of this modern technology the old school buildings have gained a huge central covered court with dappled daylighting and new wide balconies providing new circulation around this new heart to the school.

In the centre of this great space sits an extraordinary new school library and auditorium in the shape of a giant wooden egg *(Figures 13.06, 13.07)*. Designed with Gordon Cowley of Cowley Structural Timberwork, this independent structure is built using a modified geodesic grid *(see Section 4.1.3)* of larch poles, connected via Cowley steel connectors *(Figure 13.08)* into aluminium nodes. This frame is then clad in triangular panels of birch plywood on the outside and inside faces, with integral acoustic treatment.

**Figure 13.10
Steam-bent birch
plywood seats.**
Photo: Michael Mack

Awards

Wood Awards 2004
Structural award for the
overall design

Innovation award for the
Cowley connector

Credits

Client
Mayor and Burgesses of
Southwark

Architect
De Rijke Marsh Morgan
(dRMM)

Structural engineer
Michael Hadi Associates

Environmental engineer
Fulcrum

Acoustic consultant
Fleming & Barron

Main contractor
Galliford Try

Auditorium Joinery and frame
Cowley Structural
Timberwork

Artist
Atelier van Lieshout

In the auditorium *(Figure 13.09)* the raked seating is made of steam-bent birch plywood bench forms *(Figure 13.10)* set over the carpeted stepped floor. Additional acoustic panels of Melatech foam are attached directly to the inside panels of the domed roof to fine-tune the acoustic performance. Floating triangular acoustic reflectors of birch plywood are suspended within the space to adjust the sound around the stage.

This auditorium is entered at first floor level from the new circulation balconies, and the school library is tucked neatly under the raked seating, with its own entrance at ground level.

The whole project has been highly successful, with the new covered court providing a new heart and a unity to the school, which is immediately apparent to pupils and visitors as they move around the circulation spaces. Inside this space sits the marvellous wooden auditorium egg, defining and enlivening the space with exemplary simplicity and directness of form.

The use of sustainable larch poles for the structure of the auditorium, and the cladding and seating made of birch plywood, ensure that this building is highly sustainable and enjoys a feeling of warmth and lightness.

The auditorium has won two awards for excellence, but more importantly the effect on the school has been dramatic, with a strong new sense of identity. The whole atmosphere of the school has changed to one of success, with the attendance and academic standards improving by leaps and bounds.

CASE STUDY

14

The David Douglas Pavilion, Pitlochry, Perthshire

Peter Ross

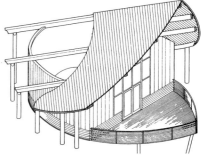

Figure 14.05 *(opposite page)*
The roof shingles.

Figure 14.01 *(left)*
**Rear view of the Pavilion
from the south.**

Figure 14.02 *(above)*
Diagram of the roof structure.

Figure 14.03 *(above)*
A scarf joint in a roof purlin.

David Douglas is the most famous of the 19th century plant collectors. In 1825 he made an expedition to Canada and returned with seeds of the Douglas fir, named after him, and the Sitka spruce. He was therefore responsible for introducing to Europe the two species which make up the bulk of our present-day constructional timber. This commemorative Pavilion has been designed by Gaia Architects Aberfeldy in the grounds of a new Scottish Plant Collectors' Garden at Pitlochry, which celebrates 300 years of Scottish botanical exploration.

The Garden is situated to the rear of the Pitlochry Festival Theatre and was created from a two-hectare area of mature woodland. Approaching the rear of the Pavilion from the south, it is nestled among trees – one so close that the roof profile has been locally modified *(Figure 14.01)*. The entire structure is built of wood – most of it Douglas fir, and all grown in Scotland. The building's appearance is dominated by the roof, a steep duo-pitch tilted down to the rear with a curved perimeter, and resembling a folded leaf *(Figure 14.02)*. It is supported on a series of purlins running front-to-back, overlain with nailed tongued and grooved boards which create a stiff diaphragm, and also form the Pavilion ceiling. The longest are jointed in the span by face-halved and bladed scarfs – see *Figure 14.03* and *Chapter 3, Figure 3.05*.

The purlins in turn rest on 300 mm diameter posts of peeled logs, each one joined at the top with a traditional double-pegged tenon, and lifted clear of the ground at the base by a modern steel shoe *(Figure 14.04)*. All of the structural timber is Douglas fir.

The roof surface is covered with 150 mm x 450 mm larch shingles, set apart by 6mm for ventilation, and (except at the eaves and the ridge) cut with chevron tails. The use of a moderately durable timber for shingles is

Figure 14.06
View from the north.

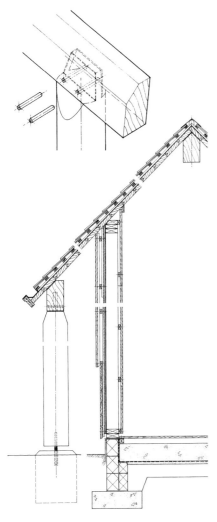

Figure 14.04
Section through the roof and wall.

The drawings were first published in The Architect's Journal in an article written by Susan Dawson as part of a 'Timber in Architecture' supplement, sponsored by wood for good.

admittedly experimental, but the installation is well detailed, and the roof pitch is steep *(Figure 14.05)*. The ridge is in copper sheeting, so rainwater running down the roof would contain a small amount of copper sulphate in solution, discouraging the build-up of moss and algae. The gutter is lead-lined, with a profile dictated by the shape, which leaves the low points between posts. The outlets discharge down Japanese chains.

The walls stand within the line of the posts, and are framed and clad externally with timber boarding. The interior is a simple exhibition space, lined to the sides and the rear with vertical Douglas fir boards, slightly rounded on face. The north wall rises at its centre with the pitch of the roof, and contains two large glazed doors which open onto a viewing deck, sheltered by the overhang of the roof. From here, it suddenly becomes apparent that the Pavilion is actually built on the brink of a steep embankment *(Figure 14.06)*, giving views over the gardens to the hills in the distance.

Awards

Dundee Institute of Architects 2003
  Commendation award

Credits

Client
  Forestry Commission

Architect
  Gaia Architects Aberfeldy

Framer
  Carpenter Oak and Woodland Co.

15

CASE STUDY
Alnwick Castle Visitor Centre
Giles Downes

Figure 15.03 *(previous page)*
View down the cascade to the buildings in the distance.
Photo: Giles Downes

Opened in 2002 by HRH the Prince of Wales, the Alnwick Castle Garden has gone from strength to strength and is now the third most visited paid-entry garden in the UK, after Kew Gardens and Wisley.

Originally the vision of the Duchess of Northumberland, the Gardens occupy a formerly derelict 12 acre walled site close to Alnwick Castle in Northumberland. They were designed by Jacques and Peter Wirtz and include the Grand Cascade, the largest water feature of its kind in the UK, as well as extensive pleached tree walks over arched timber frames to either side and a wide range of other garden features.

The site had previously been set out as ornamental gardens in the 19th century, designed by W A Nesfield, but nothing remains of these other than

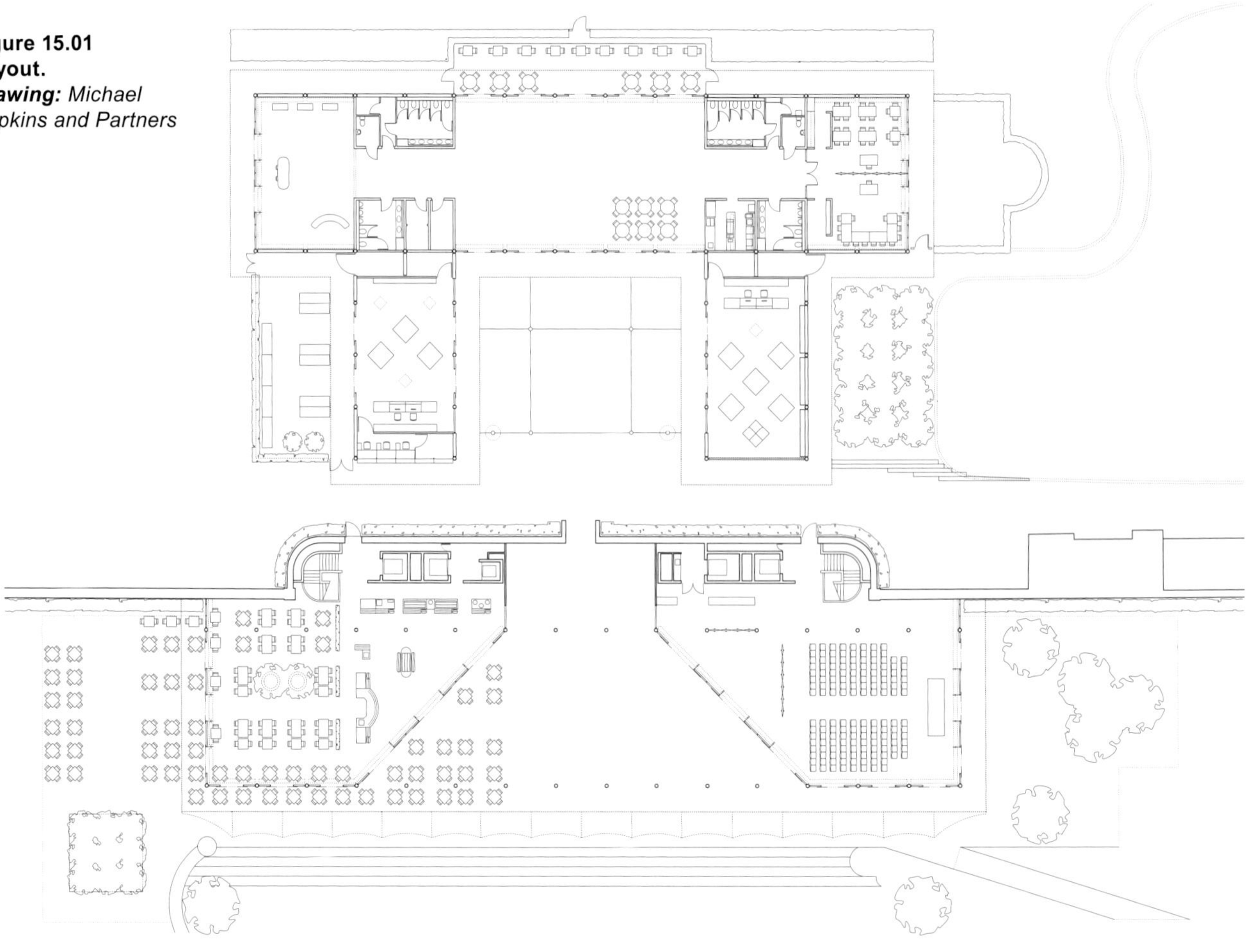

Figure 15.01
Layout.
Drawing: Michael Hopkins and Partners

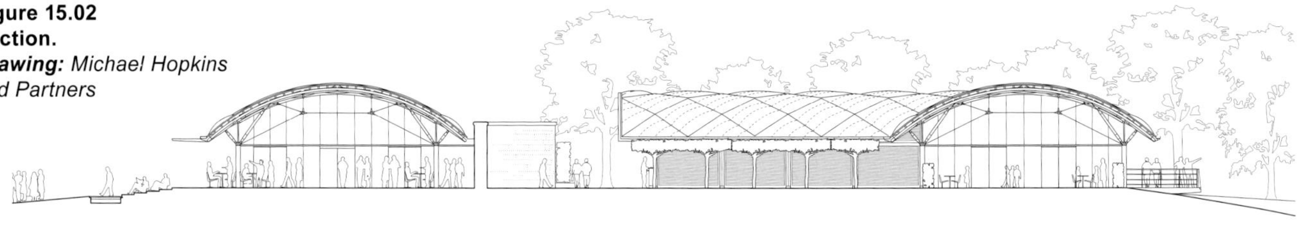

Figure 15.02
Section.
Drawing: Michael Hopkins and Partners

the listed embankments on either side of where the new Cascade now sits, together with the base of an old pavilion set on this axis against the 18th century wall at the bottom of the site.

Part of the plan for the new gardens was the provision of a new Pavilion on this site together with a Visitor Centre and Shop *(Figure 15.01)*. Michael Hopkins & Partners were appointed as architects for this project, which was completed and opened to the public in April 2006.

The new buildings lie to either side of the 18th century garden wall and take the form of linked shallow barrel vaults *(Figure 15.02)*. These are made up of lightweight timber diagonal grid structures that have been developed by Michael Hopkins & Partners and the engineers Buro Happold over a series of previous projects including Portcullis House *(see Case Study 12)* and Norwich Cathedral refectory *(see Case Study 9)*.

The check-in, visitor centre and shops are on the outside of the wall arranged in a U-shaped plan of three vaults around a central courtyard.

All the buildings are roofed in PTFE (Polytetrafluoroethylene) and ETFE (Ethylene tetrafluoroethylene) foil cushions *(Figure 15.02)*, stretched between the frames of the diagonal timber vault structures. These cushions are kept permanently inflated by a small supply of air under pressure. They provide a very lightweight rigid roof with the trapped air providing thermal insulation. The cushions are treated with different degrees of frit to control solar gain and daylight.

The main Visitor Centre building lies to the north, parallel with the old wall and contains a small café, WCs, teaching rooms, and central open space for lectures, exhibitions and demonstrations. This opens out to a shallow terrace overlooking the main Castle grounds to the north. The roof cushions to this space have 70% fritting and the walls are made up of panels of horizontal timber boarding together with fixed and sliding glazed screens.

The two small vaults at right angles are joined as hips into this main vault, following the lines of the diagonal structural grid as roof valleys. These house a Garden shop and a Souvenir shop respectively to either side of the central open courtyard, which provides a sheltered meeting place for visitors before entering the main gardens through an opening in the old listed Wall.

Once through the Wall a panoramic view on the central axis of the Grand Cascade opens up directly ahead, framed by the timber columns of the main pavilion building *(Figure 15.03)*.

Here the structural grid of the vault is really shown to advantage with translucent ETFE cushions allowing an impression of the sky beyond the frame. In contrast to previous similar buildings, this frame is made of English larch from Wiltshire. The tapered rectilinear frame members are laminated from larch timber in pairs to either side of central steel flitch plates *(see Section 3.2)* which provide fixing at the ends into tubular joint nodes. The roof grid is supported on diagonal turned larch struts spreading from the top of the turned columns. Both struts and columns have been sawn in half after turning to allow central steel flitch plates to be fitted. The vault is braced

Figure 15.04
A view of the shops.
Photo: Giles Downes

with steel tension cables and rods to make up cable trusses, leaving the timber structure and supporting columns to be as light as possible.

The whole central section of the pavilion building is open-sided, providing a covered terrace area to make the most of this marvellous view of the gardens. To either side diagonal walls, following the line of the diagonal roof grid, enclose the Restaurant to the west and the main multi-function Pavilion Room to the east.

The outer walls to the buildings are made up of full-height glazed panels *(Figure 15.04)* or horizontally boarded timber panels framed with horizontal steel work at the eaves and the level of the springing point of the vaults.

The main Pavilion sits over a basement, which contains service areas and kitchens and also an unusual sustainable rock store, which provides thermal inertia to make up for the lightweight nature of the new buildings, and provides mass storage for night time cooling which can pre-temper ventilation air during the day. The sustainable servicing of the building includes

geothermal boreholes and heat pumps to provide water for under-floor heating in the winter.

The overall effect of the buildings is relatively restrained with a feeling of warmth and lightness rather like a summer garden marquee *(Figure 15.05)*, as well as fitting directly into the English tradition of Grand Garden Pavilions and Conservatories.

Michael Hopkins and Partners have made a positive benefit out of the constraints of the listed features and historic background, so that the new buildings made the most of this magnificent site, adding to the attraction of the gardens without trying to compete with the flamboyant style of the gardens themselves.

Both the Alnwick Gardens and the new Pavilion and Visitor Centre have been extremely successful, wildly exceeding the projected visitor numbers but still managing those visitors well.

Figure 15.05
A view of the terrace.
Photo: Giles Downes

Formby Pool, Lancashire

Peter Ross

The client for the pool, the Formby Land Trust, had been set up to realise the project on a central site to the south of the High Street, on land formerly occupied by a football club. Feilden Clegg Bradley, the architects for the project, were appointed as the result of a limited competition – the Trust were impressed by their submission, which focussed on site use as well as the pool, and which pointed out the added amenity of a landscaped surround. And so the concept of 'the pool in the park' was born.

The plan form is very disciplined and consists of two adjacent rectangles (*Figure 16.03*). The larger contains the main pool, the learner pool and the café, the latter connected to an external terrace. The enclosure is a timber frame, with a roof supported by a series of bowstring trusses in Kerto® (a proprietary form of LVL – *see section 2.3.3*) with their steel tension rods ('strings') connected to flitched plates dowelled into position (*Figure 16.04*). Each truss stands on a Kerto® column, most of which are abruptly cut off above a ribbon window which runs around the three external sides of the building at ground level (*Figure 16.01*). Above the window, a concealed truss, also formed of timber, transfers the roof loads to principal columns some 10 metres apart, set inside the glazing line. Internally the truss is clad with acoustic panels formed from spaced battens of clear Douglas fir with mineral wool behind. Externally the truss is clad with vertical planks of oak, which will weather to silver grey (*Figure 16.02*).

Daylight is admitted at high level by eight rooflights and a clerestory which increases in height towards the north. As a result, the roof has a ploughshare twist, giving the building an increased presence when seen from the High Street (*Figure 16.02*). Structural stability is achieved by means of a Kerto® roof diaphragm exposed as the pool ceiling, and anchored to the lower building.

The lower service building contains the pool plant, changing facilities, entrance hall (neatly aligned with the café), kitchen, and a fitness suite. Walls are in blockwork, with a roof deck of Kerto® supported on timber I-beams cantilevered to the east, to form a projecting entrance canopy. Cladding generally consists of closely-spaced vertical battens of clear Douglas fir, with copper sheeting for the fitness suite.

A visitor cannot but be aware that this is a building constructed primarily from timber. There is a nice hierarchy in the use of the different species – cladding fully exposed to the weather is of oak; in protected external situations it is of Douglas fir. The internal structural elements of Kerto® are, of course, in spruce. In addition, there is no denying the impact of the 80 metre long ribbon window, which so successfully relates the pool and café to the external landscaped areas (*Figure 16.01*).

The building is modernist throughout, succeeding without the fig-leaf of ornament because great care has been taken with the details and the general standard of workmanship is high. Thus, the doors to the plant room are 'lost' by continuing the Douglas fir battens across them (*Figure 16.05*), and all the signage is coordinated. There are no display notices, indicating for example the building's function or the entrance location, for none are needed. It is a building which has a clear and logical design, in which the structural elements are seamlessly integrated into the overall concept.

Figure 16.01 *(opposite page)*
The pools, with the café to the rear. The roof is supported by closely-spaced bowstring trusses, interspersed with eight rooflights. The glazing is a continuous 2.4 metre high band, set at floor level and leading the eye to the landscaped areas beyond.
Photo: Dennis Gilbert / VIEW

Figure 16.02
The building seen from the High Street. It is set close to the eastern boundary, with undulating grassland and planting as a reference to Formby Sands, some two miles away.

Figure 16.05
The covered access walkway, with wall cladding of closely-spaced Douglas fir battens effectively concealing the service doors.

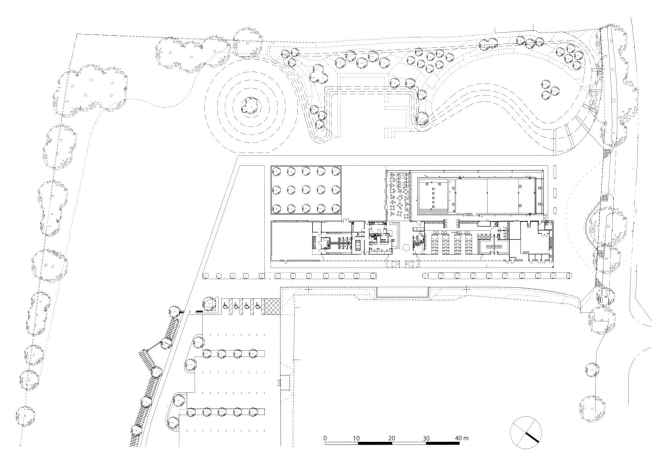

Figure 16.03
Ground floor plan.
Drawing: Feilden Clegg Bradley

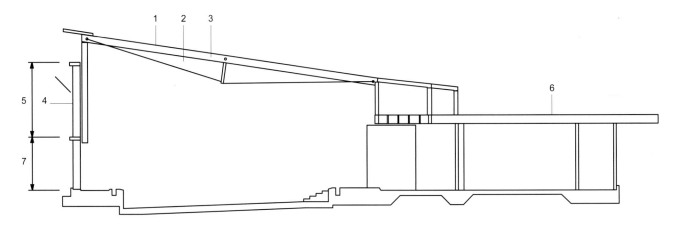

Figure 16.04
Section.
Drawing: Feilden Clegg Bradley

1 15m x 1.2m Kerto LVL (Laminated veneer lumber) deck panels joined along top of truss

2 Bow string truss: top boom of 140 x 315mm Kerto LVL, 100 x 100mm LVL strut & 24mm dia steel tie rod. Trussed run at 1.2m centres

3 Truss flitched to LVL posts at 1.2m centres

4 Composite steel and timber columns at 10.8m centres

5 Line of 50mm long concealed glulam Pratt trusses supported on composite columns at 10.8m centres

6 Ply diaphram roof deck

7 2.1m high glazed wall in concealed frame

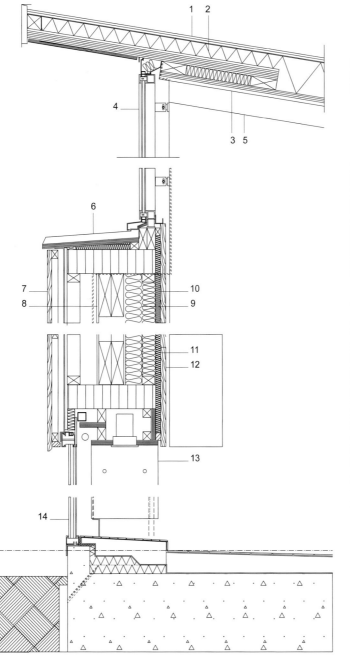

Figure 16.05
Section.
Drawing: Feilden Clegg Bradley

1 Copper sheet roof covering

2 Foamed glass insulation on
bitumen membrane

3 15m x 1.2m Kerto LVL deck panels

4 Double-glazed clerestory

5 140 x 315mm Kerto LVL top boom of
bow string truss flitched to LVL post at
1.2m centres

6 Copper sill

7 Vertical European oak weatherboards
on horizontal battens at 600mm centres

8 Concealed glulam truss

9 Rigid mineral wool insulation

10 Vapour control layer

11 Tissue-faced mineral wool insulation
for acoustic damping

12 Douglas fir battens as wall lining

13 Composite steel & timber columns at
10.8m centres

14 Façade of 2.1m high frameless glass
panels

17

Mossbourne Community Academy, Hackney, East London

Peter Ross

The Mossbourne Community Academy in East London was completed in 2005, and replaces an earlier school building on an unpromising triangle of land, bounded on two sides by railway lines. The response by the architects, the Richard Rogers Partnership, is probably unique in the field of education. A V-shaped building, deliberately turning its back on the railway, is made up of two elements – an outer blockwork diaphragm wall, imperforate except for fire exits, shielding a muscular three-storey timber frame containing the classrooms *(Figures 17.01, 17.02)*.

The frame is made entirely from whitewood glulams. Floor beams at 1.2 m centres span 9 m between the front and rear frames, comprising paired posts which clasp primary beams *(Figure 17.03)*. The primary beams are linked by bridging beams of smaller depth, giving a satisfactory rhythm to the long elevations, which might otherwise tend to be monotonous.

The building face is set back some 1.5 m from the front frames, allowing walkways to be installed *(Figure 17.04)*. These are open grids in galvanised steel, and act as fire escape routes from the classrooms, and as bris-soleil to the windows below *(Figure 17.05)*. The walkways are connected to ground level by externally-hung steel stairs suspended from extended cantilevers at roof level, echoing the escalator details at Centre Pompidou in Paris (also by Richard Rogers with Renzo Piano).

Most of the timber frame – the largest in the UK to date – lies inside the external envelope of the building. In view of this, the glulams were fabricated in whitewood. However, the ends of the beams, and their supporting

Figure 17.03
A primary beam, resting on spacer blocks bolted between the posts.

Figure 17.04
Drawing: Rogers Stirk Harbour + Partners

1 Aluminium-framed vertical-sliding double-glazed sash window
2 Electrically operated glazed vents between timber secondaries
3 Perforated metal acoustic absorbers suspended from Holorib deck
4 Raised floor
5 100mm concrete on Holorib deck
6 Secondary glulam beams
7 Primary glulam beams
8 Paired glulam columns
9 Galvanised panel as solar protection
10 Galvanised steel handrail and panels as external walkways
11 Galvanised steel and concrete column bases
12 Cloisters
13 Syphonic drainage system
14 Alumimium-clad timber doors as controlled access and fire escape
15 Double-glazed fire escape doors from each classroom
16 Hardwood timber copings
17 Paving and pebbles on rigidboard insulation on waterproofing
18 Spandrel cladding panels: backpainted glass externally and ppc aluminium internally
19 Up/down-lighters suspended from Holorib deck

Figure 17.05
A first floor walkway.

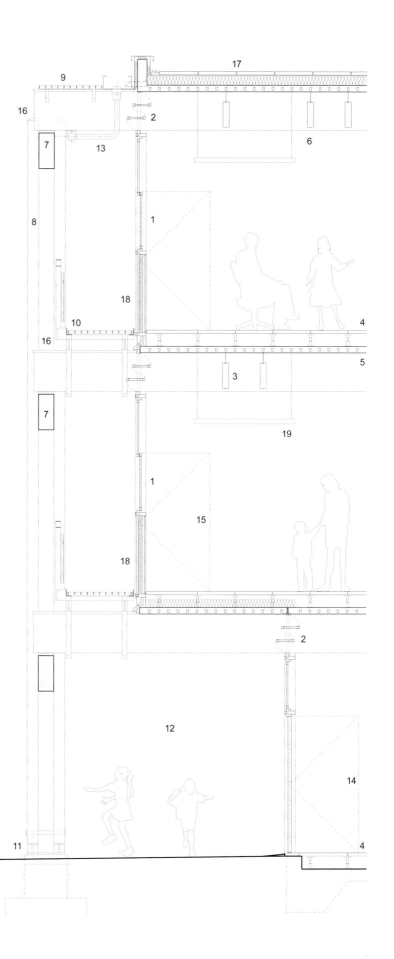

frames, are exposed to the weather, and great care has therefore been taken with the detailing, which includes the following provisions:

- The column tops and the top surfaces of the beams have a hardwood capping, with weathered falls. (The remaining surfaces are all vertical and free-draining).

- The bolt-holes are all sealed with washers.

- The beam bearing points are lifted up on hardwood packs to minimise the contact area, thus reducing the potential for water retention.

- The faces of the columns are lifted clear of the ground on steel brackets.

- A moisture-repellent coating (by Sadolin) is applied to all the external surfaces. This will need to be re-applied as a maintenance regime, but access to the frame from the balconies is relatively easy.

Two pairs of posts and their primary beams were assembled flat on the ground as H-frames, and each then lifted up into the vertical to receive the cross-beams. The floors themselves are of composite construction: profiled metal formwork is laid across the beams, and held in position by shear studs. A 100 mm thick concrete deck is then cast, which acts together with the beams in the conventional manner. This concrete/timber combination is more seen on the continent than in the UK, where it is relatively rare. A raised floor is installed above for service distribution, but the thickness of the floor and the beam dimensions ensure a one-hour period of fire-resistance without the need for additional protection or a suspended ceiling below, *(Figure 17.06)*. The floor as a whole achieves a satisfactory 'solid' feel underfoot.

The layout of the external wall is related to the module generated by the floor construction with electrically-operated glazed vents set at high level between the cross-beams with adjustable sash-type windows below. Purpose-built wind towers assist with natural ventilation as well as night cooling, eliminating the need for air conditioning plant.

The use of glulam for a frame which would conventionally be of steel or concrete marks a step forward for timber in public construction.

Figure 17.06
A classroom 'interior', looking toward the internal corridor. The floor beams, and the profiled metal formwork, are exposed at ceiling level.

Awards

RIBA Award 2005

Civic Trust Award 2006
for 'a high standard of planning and architecture'

Credits

Client
Mossbourne Community Trust/ DfES

Architect
Rogers Stirk Harbour + Partners

Structural engineer
Whitby Bird

Main contractor
MACE

18

Globe Theatre, London

Peter Ross

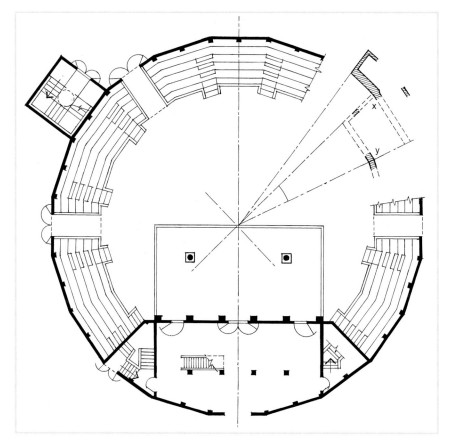

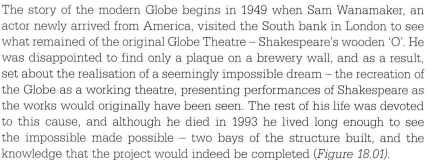

Figure 18.02 *(left)*
Plan of the Globe, with archaeological excavations superimposed.
Although the exposed area was small, the changes in footing alignment at **(x)** and **(y)** allowed the determination of the overall building diameter and gallery width, and confirmed the plan form as a twenty-sided polygon. A stair-tower footing was also found, which was enlarged in the rebuild to meet current regulations.
After Mulryne and Shewring

The story of the modern Globe begins in 1949 when Sam Wanamaker, an actor newly arrived from America, visited the South bank in London to see what remained of the original Globe Theatre – Shakespeare's wooden 'O'. He was disappointed to find only a plaque on a brewery wall, and as a result, set about the realisation of a seemingly impossible dream – the recreation of the Globe as a working theatre, presenting performances of Shakespeare as the works would originally have been seen. The rest of his life was devoted to this cause, and although he died in 1993 he lived long enough to see the impossible made possible – two bays of the structure built, and the knowledge that the project would indeed be completed *(Figure 18.01)*.

In 1970 the Shakespeare Globe Trust was formed, and a professional team assembled. Initially this was made up of Pentagram Design, architects, and Buro Happold, structural engineers, who were later joined by Peter McCurdy as the Master Carpenter. The first Globe Theatre dated from 1599, using timber from an earlier theatre in Shoreditch. It burnt down 1613, and was rebuilt, only to be closed down by the Puritans in 1642, and demolished soon after. Thus direct evidence of the construction was almost non-existent, and the team spent much time, aided by historians, researching various fields of information.

In brief summary the investigations uncovered:

- A tantalizingly small area of the original footings, the remainder being covered by existing buildings. Nevertheless, the surviving fragment included an external angle and stair tower *(Figure 18.02)*.

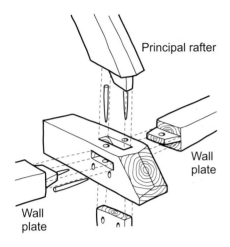

Principal rafter

Wall plate

Wall plate

Figure 18.03
The jointing of the wall plates into the tie beam at roof level. It is not possible to peg the principal rafter, as much of the timber at the heart of the joint in the tie beam has been cut away to form the mortices.

- An engraving by Wenceslaus Hollar, including the second Globe, made from the tower of St Mary Overy (now Southwark Cathedral).

- The Fortune contract, a detailed description of a theatre similar to the Globe, and built by Peter Street, the carpenter of the Globe, a year later.

- Surviving buildings of the period, particularly those with polygonal plans, such as marker crosses, chapter houses and dovecotes.

After a considerable period of research and discussion, a consensus was achieved on the construction form which could best fit the available evidence. This was a twenty-sided polygon, of overall dimension 100 feet (30 m), and three storeys high. The structure is essentially a series of radial cross frames, joined by concentric floor and roof members. At the back of each frame is a single full-height post, giving robustness to the structure, while storey-height posts at the front stand on jettied summer beams. There was no definitive information on bracing, but conventional bracing at high level in each storey could easily be fitted to the cross frames and rear wall. Braces fitted across the front posts would obviously interfere with sight lines, but the structural engineers were satisfied that the stiffness of the back wall, together with the diaphragm stiffness of the floor, would allow them to be omitted.

The aim was to strive for authenticity in form and construction. The first Globe would undoubtedly have been constructed in green oak, for the reasons given in *Section 3.1*. Four hundred years later, those reasons are still valid, and so the use of green oak for the modern frame was historically correct as well as being the practical option.

Polygonal buildings present jointing problems *(Figure 18.03)*. In conventional rectangular buildings, long members, such as the roof plate at roof level, are jointed away from the frame because life is easier that way. This option does

Figure 18.04
Timber shrinks across the grain as it dries, an effect most pronounced in oak. The three specimens (right) were cut green, and allowed to dry out.

a Shows that tangential shrinkage is almost twice radial shrinkage, and has pulled the square to a diamond shape. Since there is no resistance to the shrinkage, there is no fissure

b When the centre of the tree is included – 'boxed heart' – the gradually developing shrinkage stress eventually causes a fissure to develop at the weakest (generally, as here, shortest) section

c Drilling out the heart relieves, to a large extent, the circumferential stresses, reducing the tendency to fissure.

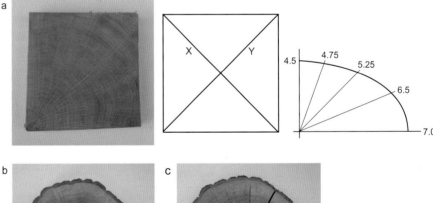

Figure 18.05 *(above)*
The major fissure in one of the ground floor posts.

Figure 18.06 *(top left)*
Newel post with boxed heart showing fissures. The handrails, being quarter-sawn and excluding the heart, have few fissures (the polish on the top of the post is entirely due to hand contact).

Figure 18.07 *(top middle)*
Slight twist at the base of one of the posts in the north-east corner.

Figure 18.09 *(left)*
One of the two stage columns, looking up at the 'heavens'. They are painted to resemble marble and topped with elaborate Corinthian capitals. The stage as a whole, literally the focus of the theatre, is a riot of 'early Rennaisance' decoration.

not exist for the polygonal building, and so the tie beam was run over the top of the post, with the wall plates tenoned in from either side. It was still possible to tenon the principal rafter into the tie beam, but there was no way of pegging it. Fortunately, an analysis showed that wind uplift would never exceed the dead weight, and so in this case a peg was not necessary.

Authenticity in construction included wattle and daub infill panels, and (after a long regulatory discussion) a roof of thatch. Inevitable compromises included a concrete surface in the yard, escape stairs enlarged from the original dimensions, and the installation of electrical light (although there is no 'stage' lighting).

The Globe, completed in 1996, stands some 200 m from the original, and as one of the largest green oak frames built in recent years (and, incidentally, the first in the capital since the great fire of 1666), it is also a very public 'worked example' of the behaviour and appearance of green oak over time. The size of the frame means that most members contain boxed heart and so the front posts (exposed on all faces) can be seen to have one major fissure, and often a few subsidiary fissures which are the result of drying shrinkage *(Figures 18.04, 18.05)*. The ends of the newel posts show similar fissures *(Figure 18.06)*, and sometimes an end split.

There is occasional evidence of twisting – the base of one of the posts in the north-east tower has rotated slightly *(Figure 18.07)*; but the width of the

Figure 18.08
The typical wedge-shaped drying movement at the ends of the wind braces.

end tenon on the post will prevent further movement. Typical wedge-shaped gaps can be seen at the ends of the wind braces (*Figure 18.08*), caused by shrinkage in the brace width. On a small contract this would have also opened up a gap between the brace and the infill render, but the Globe, due to its size and funding requirements, was built on a relatively long timescale. This meant that many of the framing members had undergone most of their shrinkage before the panels were rendered. Nevertheless, a small amount of making good and repainting was necessary.

Figure 18.10 *(right)*
Timber in the splash zone darkened rapidly.

Figure 18.11 *(top)*
Staining from the iron nails in the door.

Figure 18.12 *(bottom)*
The sill beam, showing water marking and darkening on the planking above where 'groundlings' squat on the beam.

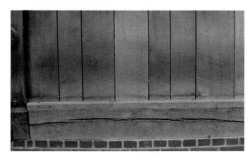

While the occurrence of fissures in the frame members could be regarded as the character of green oak construction, it was felt that they would be less acceptable in the stage columns – two of the largest pieces in the assembly, with elaborate surface decoration. In order to minimise the tendency to fissure, McCurdy and Co drilled a hole down the centre of each column, on the principle shown in *Figure 18.04*. To date, this has effectively maintained the integrity of the 'marbled' surfaces.

The natural weathering of the exposed oak surfaces has produced a range of colour changes. The external frame faces, most exposed to the sun and rain, have changed to a silver-grey (*Figures 18.07, 18.08*); while the interior timbers, afforded varying degrees of weather protection, have been affected in proportion to their exposure: the posts at the courtyard level and the floors retain virtually their original colour (*Figure 18.05*). However, the timber close to the ground in the splash zone rapidly darkened (*Figure 18.10*). Contact with iron (and rain) also produces marked staining (*Figure 18.11*).

It is also not surprising that the capacity audiences leave their mark; the newel posts (*Figure 18.06*) carry a polish which is solely due to hand contact, and the temptation for the 'groundlings' (members of the audience who stand in the open area in the yard) to squat on the sill beam of the courtyard is also recorded on the planking above (*Figure 18.12*).

Thus the oak responds, and will continue to respond, to the efffects of the weather and the audiences which fill the theatre over the summer months. Any potential client for a green oak structure who wishes to judge the appearance of an oak frame as it matures could do no better than to visit this simultaneously ancient and modern building.

Awards

Carpenters' Award 1997

Credits

Client
The Globe Theatre Trust

Architect
Pentagram

Structural engineer
Buro Happold

Framer
Peter McCurdy and Co.

19

Sage Concert Hall, Gateshead

Giles Downes

Figure 19.03 *(previous page)*
External view.
Photo: *Nigel Young / Foster + Partners*

The North Music Trust was set up by Gateshead Borough Council to be the client for this new centre of music for the Northeast of England, located in Gateshead on the banks of the River Tyne.

After 18 months of public consultation the Trust decided on an inclusive centre that would be the home not only for the Northern Sinfonia, one of Europe's finest orchestras, but also for Folkworks, which was established in 1988 by Ros Rigby and Alistair Anderson as the folk music development agency for the North of England. It has now been transformed into an organisation on a par with the Sinfonia, running workshops, summer schools, concerts, and offering the UK's first degree course in folk and traditional music.

The new building by Foster and Partners, completed in 2004, includes three state of the art auditoria *(Figure 19.01)*, side by side under a sweeping undulating steel and glass shell roof *(Figure 19.02)*.

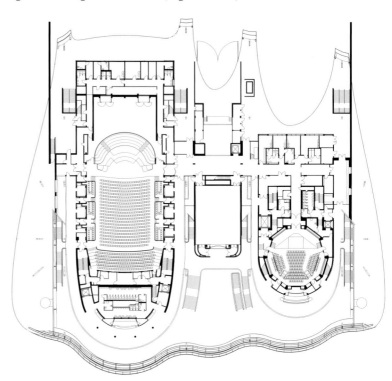

Figure 19.01
Plan.
Drawing: *Foster + Partners*

The site is steeply sloping down to the River Tyne and the building takes advantage of this to place supporting areas, including the music school, recording studios and ancillary spaces in a semi basement dug into the hillside. Daylight filters in from the north side from the huge glazed wall fronting the main public concourse above. This north-facing glazed wall gives a marvellous sense of light and spaciousness to the concourse on the upper level, with dramatic views out across the river to the Millennium Bridge and the Baltic Centre for Contemporary Arts beyond *(Figure 19.03)*.

The main criterion for the building was to achieve the highest acoustic performance for the auditoria. In order to provide the acoustic isolation that was required, the three auditoria shells are built of dense concrete and heavy

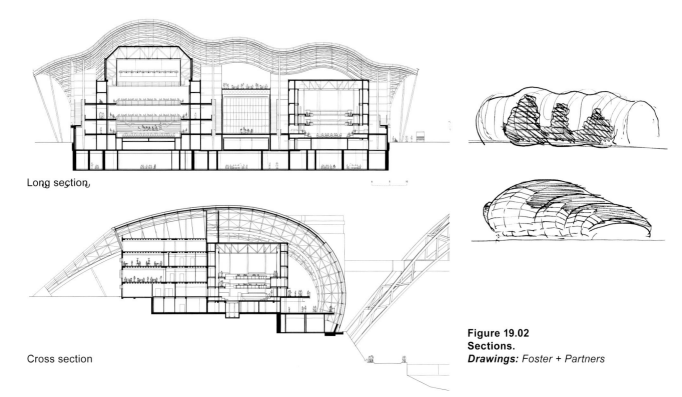

Long section

Cross section

**Figure 19.02
Sections.**
Drawings: Foster + Partners

block work isolated from each other. They sit in line under the overarching roof, separated by rising stairs with cantilevered curvilinear decks and an overhanging concourse which provide circulation and access to upper circle seating for the auditoria and to bars, cafeterias and WCs.

To unify these public spaces, the outer curving surfaces are all finished in cool smooth white render throughout. Inside the auditoria the overriding impression is the warmth of natural timber finishes *(Figure 19.04)*.

The huge orchestral hall is large enough to seat 1700 people, but so well lit and clearly organised that it gives a sense of intimacy belying its size. It is finished throughout in American white ash which was chosen for its pale honey colour, straight grain, and controlled performance characteristics. This is matched with similar-coloured birch finished plywood.

The acoustic absorption and resonance of wood make it the perfect finish for auditoria in order to achieve the best possible acoustics, and here timber is used in several different forms to maintain a uniform appearance throughout while fulfilling differing roles.

Following detailed design advice from Arup Acoustics, the main walls are simply finished in solid ash battens of varying depths, fixed vertically over a built-up backing of solid MDF *(see Section 2.3.6)* in order to provide an undulating wall surface to give the optimum diffusion of sound. *(Figure 19.04)*.

Seat shells are of birch plywood, as are the acoustically shaped fronts to the seating balconies. These are formed of double layers of 24 mm thick birch plywood to give sufficient weight, not just for strength but to provide enough stiffness and inertia to avoid uncontrolled reverberation.

Figure 19.04
The rear wall is clad with vertical timber battens of varying depths, fixed over a built-up backing of solid MDF to provide an optimum diffusion of sound. The curved balcony fronts are formed of horizontal timber slats, with a horizontal slot cut in the outer face as an acoustic pocket for sound diffusion.

Awards

Wood Awards 2005
Commercial and Public Access Buildings award

Credits

Client
Gateshead Council, North Music Trust

Architect
Foster & Partners

Acoustic Engineer
Arup Acoustic

Structural engineer
Connell Matt McDonald

Main Contractor
Laing O'Rourke

The curved balcony fronts *(Figure 19.04)* are made up of a series of horizontal sections, each individually fixed to a metal framework and with a horizontal slot cut in the outer face as an acoustic pocket for sound diffusion. On the corners of the balconies, special saddle shaped double-curvature panels had to be made up, laminated from 12 thicknesses of 4 mm birch ply.

The largest and most demanding elements of auditoria to produce, were the 6 moveable ceiling sound reflectors, each weighing 14 tons, which can be adjusted to tune the hall perfectly for differing performances. These are each made up of 30 large boat-shaped wooden sections arranged in ten groups of three. Each was constructed out of two layers of 6 mm marine grade birch plywood, bonded together in curved jigs and then finished with American ash veneer. Each of these hollow sections was then lined with 75 mm MDF solidly laminated to avoid pockets and to provide sufficient mass to damp sound reverberation.

By contrast the much smaller central Rehearsal Room is lined with fabric and timber sound absorption panels in a comparatively simple 10 m high box. Full-height lining panels can be moved to adjust the performance.

Finally the octagonal Recital Hall can seat an audience of 400 in the round, on three levels using stained timber finishers.

Throughout the construction period the concrete and blockwork were slowly drying out so that constant monitoring was required to control humidity and moisture content in the timber.

The building is a pleasure to visit, with an overriding sense of light and space in the concourse. The main auditorium is one of the finest in the world with great clarity of form and the highest level of acoustic performance. The use of timber in this main concert hall not only meets the most demanding acoustic criteria, but also gives the space a sense of warmth that perfectly balances its austere form.

20

CASE STUDY
King's School Library
Giles Downes

Figure 20.04 *(previous page)*
Looking into the library across the lightwell.
Photo: Martine Hamilton Knight

Figure 20.01 *(above)*
Looking out through the entrance doors of the new two-storey entrance volume.
Photo: Martine Hamilton Knight

Figure 20.02 *(right)*
The reading area on the ground floor of the book-lined lightwell.
Photo: Martine Hamilton Knight

Kings School in Worcester, under the shadow of Worcester Cathedral, consists of a historic group of buildings ranging from the 13th to the 20th century.

In 1997 the school decided to move entirely to day pupils. It commissioned Associated Architects to carry out a review of the school's operations and buildings, and prepare a master plan for the future development of the school.

From this study a phased programme of renovation, landscaping and building works was started. The Old School library had occupied a Grade 1 listed tower with access up a dark winding staircase, and the provision of a new library, which would fully comply with modern access requirements, became an important part of these new works.

A new location was chosen for the library within the lower two floors of a Victorian building, with the addition of a new 'Long Gallery' linking between two adjacent school courtyards.

A light-filled new two-storey volume *(Figure 20.01)* was built adjacent to the existing building, opening onto both upper and lower floors of the library, thus bringing additional light and a feeling of space. The Long Gallery provides the approach to the new library, which is entered via a glass and timber bridge across the new lightwell. The latter is lined with tall display shelves *(Figure 20.02)*, forming the front to a new stair down from the entrance to the lower level. On the opposite wall, the librarian's central desk overlooks the space from the upper floor with further display shelves on the wall below fronting a study room. The whole facility of 850 m^2 has full IT provision and space for a hundred reader stations.

Figure 20.03
The entrance bridge to the main library space at the upper level of the lightwell.
Photo: Martine Hamilton Knight

Awards

Wood Awards 2005
Special Small Project and Innovation award

City of Worcester Award 2006

Credits

Client
Kings School, Worcester

Architect
Associated Architects

Main contractor
Spicers

Structural engineers
Shires Consulting

Joinery
Opus Magnum and Spicers

The entrance storey on the upper floor contains the main library space *(Figures 20.03, 20.04)* with a marvellous shelving system, specially designed by the architects, constructed entirely in cantilevered 12 mm plywood shelves. The latter are invisibly supported from the rear by a simple locking form, and are vertically adjustable in 90 mm increments.

The absence of vertical supports creates a delightful horizontal floating effect that enhances the general feeling of spaciousness, and usefully allows the book stock to run on continuous shelves without interruption. It is intriguing to see how successfully this system enables the thin 12mm shelves to support the weight of the books without distortion.

The walls and piers of the Long Gallery are faced with panels of birch plywood, faced with ice birch veneer for an added richness of figure. The design in these horizontal panels deliberately gives the effect of classical stone work.

Artistic touches such as the fret-cut letters of a Greek quotation (translated in etched lettering on adjacent glazed panels) add an extra level of meaning to this space.

The librarians' station is a tour de force of accuracy and craftsmanship carried through purely in birch plywood sheets, fret-cut into curving strips which are assembled in alternate layers with absolute precision into an undulating contoured form.

Completed in 2006, the new library has been a great success and has formed a vibrant new heart for the school.

21

CASE STUDY
Accordia Flats, Cambridge
Giles Downes

The Accordia site, off Brooklands Avenue, is one of the largest brownfield housing sites in Cambridge. It offered a marvellous opportunity to the owners, Countryside Properties, to create new housing set in mature landscaping in this leafy suburb, opposite Cambridge University's Botanical Gardens.

The site is nine and a half hectares in extent and was previously occupied by Government Offices and defunct World War II prefabricated buildings.

Figures 21.01 *(opposite page)* **and 21.02** *(left)*
Front elevation of the heavy green oak frame within which some modules have been left open while elegant steel-framed, timber-decked balconies project outward from others.
Photos: Giles Downes

Awards

Wood Awards 2007
Highly commended in the
Private category

RIBA Stirling Prize 2008

Credits

Client
Countryside Properties plc

Architect
Feilden Clegg Bradley

Contractor
Kajima Construction (UK) ltd

Structural engineer
Richard Jackson

Feilden Clegg Bradley Architects were commissioned to carry out the master planning for the site for new housing and to complete some of the buildings, with others to be designed by the architectural practices Maccreanor Lavington and Alison Brooks.

Restrictive Covenants, existing mature landscape and planning constraints limited the housing numbers and density, which was eventually approved at 40 dwellings per hectare overall. This gave a total of 212 houses in two to three storey terraces, and 166 flats in blocks up to seven storeys.

Feilden Clegg Bradley have developed a full façade-height external timber balcony frame as one motif for these flats. They had incorporated this design for one of the earlier apartment blocks close to Brooklands Avenue, using green oak to provide a separate exposed structural frame on a large scale with horizontal members at floor levels to carry balconies on one side of this block.

They have also more recently re-used this motif in a more developed form for one of the larger apartment blocks, set within the site. This block looks out to the north towards the mature trees and stream which run along the northern edge of the site. To the east it overlooks a large open public green space bordering a small lake to the north.

To take advantage of these magnificent views, the architects have again designed a full height external structural frame in heavy green oak sections along the length of these two sides. Within this frame they have left some floors open but on others have projected more elegant individual steel-framed, timber-decked balconies with timber and glass balustrades *(Figures 21.01, 21.02)*.

The green oak frame is connected with bolted steel flitch plates *(see Section 3.2)* rather than traditional joints, but provides a rustic effect to complement the mature tree planting and landscape of the site. The oak is at present rather patchily blackened but will eventually weather to an even silver grey.

Rather appropriately this frame sits over the extended ground floor base, which is occupied by parking and is faced with plain dry stone walling (the stones are loose-laid within narrow stainless steel wire gabions) to extend the rustic effect. A level of contradiction and playfulness is added to the design through this wall becoming non-loadbearing and being kept so thin as to be partially see-through, letting light and air through the cracks into the car park behind.

The heavy oak frame above is designed in a similar manner so that the actual balconies are much lighter and more elegant than the frame which carries them, and only occupy a part of it, leaving the rest open like a giant climbing frame. This of course also allows more light into the apartments behind.

The overall effect of the building design combines serious and playful intentions in one image and one design, which will in due course blend well into the landscape of this magnificent site. The building is well executed and is part of a very successful new overall housing development in Cambridge.

Ealing Bridge, London

Peter Ross

Figure 22.01 *(previous page)*
Ealing Bridge.

In 1998, the Green Oak Carpentry Company was commissioned by Ealing Borough Council to rebuild a bridge across the Grand Union Canal at Norththolt, re-establishing an access route to a recreational area for local residents. The brief was to provide a robust structure with a long design life, which needed minimum maintenance.

The approach ramps and abutments already existed, setting the basic line and span of the bridge, although the abutments themselves were to be rebuilt. The bridge would have a width of 1.9 m, a clear span of 16.5 m, and an imposed loading of 4 kN/m². Simple beams of this span would be beyond economic supply, but the obvious alternative of upstanding trusses would require a large number of joints to be made. There remained the possibility of an arch, if it could be made flat enough to walk over *(Figure 22.01)*.

The project engineer checked an arch with a rise of only 900 mm, and concluded that two 600 mm deep by 300 mm wide carriage beams would be satisfactory, if the timber quality was reasonably high. The gradient of the deck was set to comply with requirements for disabled users (generally less than 1 in 12, with a short length less than 1 in 10 at each abutment) by running the walking surface from the top of the beams at the supports, to near the bottom at mid-span *(Figure 22.02)*.

Two butts of oak were required, each of which would need to be some 9 m long, and contain a 600 mm sapwood-free square section which, in addition, would be pre-cambered by 100 mm. Such timber required special enquiries to be made with suppliers, and obviously bore a considerable cost premium.

Since the arch was so shallow, it was necessary to check the effects of longi-tudinal shrinkage in the main beam. Normally, as stated in *Section 2.1.2*,

**Figure 22.02
Elevation and
substructure
plan.**

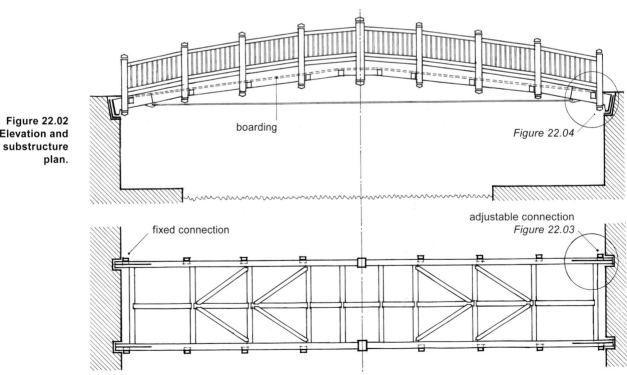

boarding

Figure 22.04

fixed connection

adjustable connection
Figure 22.03

longitudinal shrinkage is neglected, but this is a very flat arch and so the crown was further raised by 150 mm to allow for the movement. However, timber is a variable material, and it also seemed possible that slope of grain might allow a component of cross-grain shrinkage into the length, increasing the drop, and hence the abutment forces, which were already large. Hence the introduction of the tie-bars (*Figures 22.02, 22.04*), including a patented coupler called the 'techno-tensioner' (after the cartoon character Wallace's own trouser invention) which would allow the length to be adjusted under load.

As for all external structures, attention was paid to the weathering details. Water traps were avoided, or vented. Joints were cut in such a way as to allow them to drain freely, and the handrail posts were housed onto the sides of the main beams rather than morticed into the top face. This also meant that the drying movement of the beams (set heart-out) tended to tighten the bolts holding the posts in position (*Figure 22.03*). As an additional precaution, upward-sloping holes were drilled close to the carriage-spreader beam joists, with boron rods inserted and held in position with plastic plugs.

Any moisture would activate the boron, which would then dissipate into the timber. As a maintenance item, the decking boards could be lifted, and new rods inserted.

The bridge was installed on its new abutments in March 1999, using a 50-ton crane, and to everyone's relief the first canal boat proved the clearance to be satisfactory. Datum levels were marked at the crown and the supports and monitored on a six-monthly basis. After two years the drop was only 12 mm, the tensioning capability had not been used, and the tie rods became slack. It was assumed that the new abutments had settled slightly towards the canal, and since all was well, the tie-rods were removed.

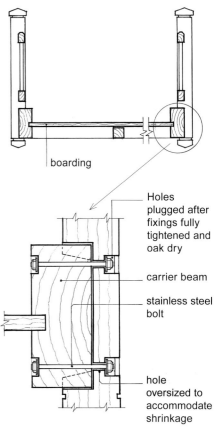

Figure 22.03
Parapet connections.

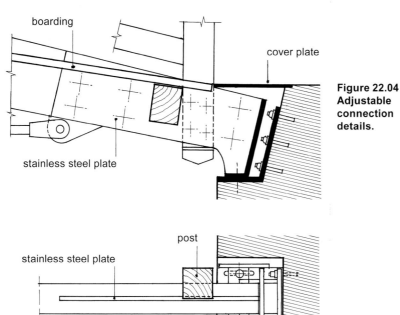

**Figure 22.04
Adjustable
connection
details.**

Credits

Client
Ealing Borough Council

Structural engineer
Ian Payne

Carpenter
The Green Oak Carpentry Company

Further reading

Publications shown by TRADA are published by TRADA Technology Limited *and are available at* www.trada.co.uk.

Chapter 1 The appeal of timber

Pryce, Will. *Architecture in Wood: a World History.* ISBN 978-0500342138. Thames and Hudson, 2005.

Slavid, Ruth. *Wood Architecture.* Hardcover, ISBN 978-1856694025, 2005. Paperback, ISBN 978-1856696067. Laurence King Publishing, 2009.

Slavid, Ruth. *Wood Houses.* ISBN 978-1856694551. Laurence King Publishing, 2006.

Stungo, Naomi. *The New Wood Architecture.* ISBN 978-1856692595. Laurence King Publishing, 2001.

Tiainen, Jussi. *Wood Architecture in Finland.* ISBN 978-9516828476. Rakennustieto Publishing, 2007.

Wilson, Peter. *New Timber Architecture in Scotland.* ISBN 978-1904320050. Arcamedia, 2007.

Wood decorative and practical. WIS 2/3-6. TRADA, 1999.

Chapter 2 The materials of construction

The general characteristics and properties of timber

Desch, H. E. and Dinwoodie, J. M. *Timber: Structure, Properties, Conversion and Use.* 7th revised edition. ISBN: 978-0333609057. Macmillan, 1996.

Durability and decay

BS 8417: 2003 *Preservation of timber – Recommendations.*

BS EN 350-2:1994 *Durability of wood and wood-based products. Natural durability of solid wood. Guide to natural durability and treatability of selected wood species of importance in Europe.*

Ridout, Brian. *Timber in Buildings: Decay, Treatment and Conservation: The Conservation Approach to Treatment.* ISBN: 978-0419188209. Taylor & Francis, 1999.

Wood Protection Association. www.wood-protection.org

Species properties

BRE. *Handbook of Softwoods.* ISBN: 0114705631. BRE Press, 1977.

Maun, K. *Handbook of Hardwoods.* ISBN: 1860814107. BRE Press, 2000.

Timbers – their properties and uses. WIS 2/3-10. TRADA, 2007.

Structural softwood sizes and grades

BS EN 1313-1:1997 *Round and sawn timber. Permitted deviations and preferred sizes. Softwood sawn timber.*

BS EN 338:2003 *Structural timber. Strength classes.*

BS EN 1194:1999 *Timber structures. Glued laminated timber. Strength classes and determination of characteristic values.*

Dry graded structural softwood. WIS 4-29. TRADA, 2002.

Glued Laminated Timber Association. www.glulam.co.uk

Joinery grades

BS EN 942: 2007 *Timber in joinery – General requirements.*

Timber in joinery. WIS 4-16. TRADA, 2002.

Sustainable sourcing

Sustainable timber sourcing. WIS 2/3-58. TRADA, 2007.

The Central Point of Expertise for Timber Procurement. www.proforest.net/cpet

Finishes

Finishes for exterior timber. WIS 2/3-1. TRADA, 2005.

Flame retardants

Flame retardant treatments for timber. WIS 2/3-3. TRADA, 2005.

Chapter 3 Connections

Adhesively-bonded timber connections. WIS 2/3-31. TRADA, 2003.

Design of structural timber connections. WIS 2/3-36. TRADA, 2003.

Fasteners for structural timber: nails, screws, bolts and dowels. WIS 2/3-52. TRADA, 2002.

Chapter 4 Applications
Roofs

Principles of pitched roof construction.
WIS 1-10. TRADA, 1993.

Trussed rafters. WIS 1-29. TRADA, 2007.

Frames

Ross, Peter; Mettem, Christopher; and Holloway, Andrew. *Green oak in construction.*
ISBN 978-1900510455. TRADA, 2007.

Twist, Huel and Lancashire, Robin. *Timber frame construction.* ISBN 978-1-900510561. 3rd edition. TRADA, 2006.

Introduction to timber frame construction.
WIS 0-3. TRADA, 2006.

Multi-storey timber frame buildings: a design guide.
ISBN 1-860816053. BRE and TRADA, 2003.

Timber frame housing: UK Structural recommendations.
ISBN 1-900510502. 3rd edition. TRADA, 2006.

Flooring

Kaczmar, Peter. *Wood flooring: A professionals' guide to installation.* ISBN 978-1900510646.
TRADA, 2009.

Decorative timber flooring. WIS 1-46. TRADA, 2004.

Windows and doors

Hislop, P. Wood windows: *Designing for high performance.*
ISBN 978-1900510622. 3rd edition. TRADA, 2009.

Timber external doors. WIS 1-47. TRADA, 2005.

External timber

Hislop, P. *External timber cladding.*
ISBN 978-1900510554. 2nd edition. TRADA, 2007.

Hislop, P. *Timber decking: the professionals' manual.*
ISBN: 1900510529. 2nd edition. TRADA, 2006.

Durability by design. WIS 4-28. TRADA, 2004.

Finishes for external timber.
WIS 2/3-1. TRADA, 2005.

Specifying timber exposed to weathering.
WIS 2/3-60. TRADA, 2008.

Timber cladding for building refurbishment.
WIS 1-50. TRADA, 2009.

Timber for landscape architecture.
WIS 1-31. TRADA, 1993.

Chapter 5 Innovation
Alternatives to chemical preservatives

Hill, Callum. *Wood modification: chemical, thermal and other processes.*
ISBN: 978-0470021729. Wiley, 2006.

Thermowood Handbook 2003.
The Finnish Thermowood Association. Available at www.thermowood.fi

Nine-storey residential building

Cross-laminated timber: An introduction for specifiers. WIS 2/3-61. TRADA, 2009.

Cross-laminated timber: Structural principles.
WIS 2/3-62. TRADA, 2009.

Thompson, Henrietta.
Stadthaus: A process revealed.
ISBN: 978-0955862069.
Murray & Sorrell FUEL, 2009.

Supermarkets frames in timber

Anderson, Jane; Shiers, David; Steele, Kristian.
The green guide to specification.
ISBN: 978-1405119610. 4th edition.
Wiley-Blackwell, 2009.